GCSE (9-1) Astronomy

A Guide for Pupils and Teachers

Fifth Edition

Nigel Marshall

This is the fifth edition of *GCSE Astronomy: A Guide for Pupils and Teachers*; it has been revised and completely modernised to meet the subject requirements of Edexcel's exciting new GCSE (9-1) specification for first examination in summer 2019 (subject code: 1AS0).

In addition to the clear, concise and accurate text, full-colour images and diagrams, and an abundance of exam hints and tips that have become the benchmark of our publications, this new edition features:

- 72 pages, 8 more than all of our previous editions,
- a full index (back by popular request),
- guidance on how to carry out observational tasks,
- extra references to further teaching and learning resources.

The GCSE (9-1) Astronomy specification, Sample Assessment Material, Course Planner, editable Scheme of Work and other teaching and learning materials can be found by on the Edexcel/Pearson website www.pearson.com (follow the links to 'Our qualifications' and 'GCSE Astronomy from 2017').

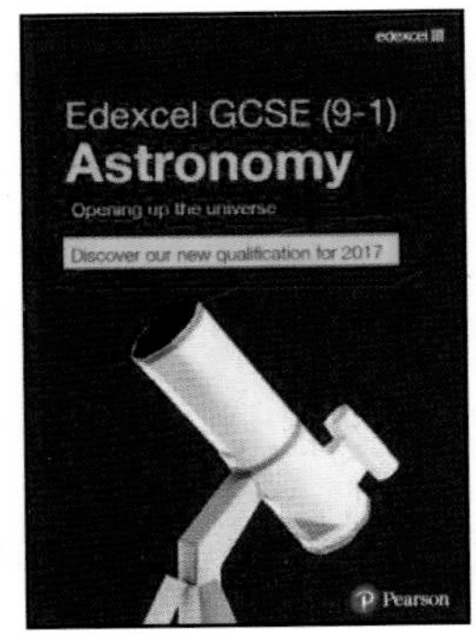

GCSE (9-1) Astronomy: A Guide for Pupils and Teachers

Guide to *Marginalia*

You'll often find these symbols in the margins: use them to improve your understanding, develop observational skills and examination technique, and explore other useful resources.

Pop Quiz

Quick-fire questions to keep you alert and test your astronomical knowledge and trivia.

Observational Tasks

Guidance and tips on how to carry out observational tasks and improve your skills and techniques.

Find Out More

Helpful resources and reference material in books, magazines, CD-ROMs and on the internet to enhance teaching and learning.

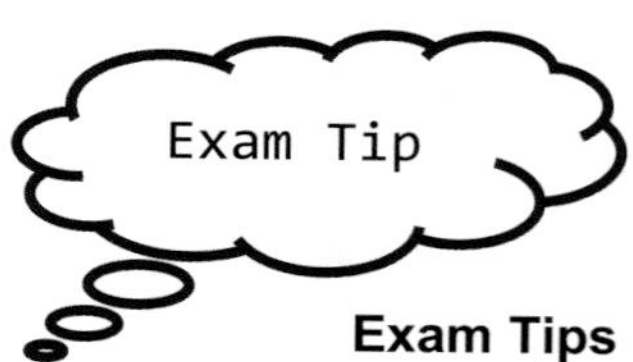

Exam Tips

Useful hints and tips from teachers and examiners to help students to gain confidence and improve examination technique.

The specification content is presented as two major themes - Naked-eye Astronomy and Telescopic Astronomy - each containing 8 topics.

The subject material in this book follows the course as set out in Edexcel's editable Scheme of Work; topics 1 - 8 will be examined in paper 1 (Naked-eye Astronomy) and topics 9 - 16 in paper 2 (Telescopic Astronomy).

'Man [and woman] *must rise above the Earth - to the top of the atmosphere and beyond - for only thus will he fully understand the world in which he* [she] *lives.'*

Socrates, Greek philosopher

GCSE Astronomy: A Guide for Pupils and Teachers is one of four major new resources from Mickledore Publishing to support the teaching and learning of GCSE (9-1) Astronomy. Details of the additional resources, including the CD-ROM *Essential Maths Skills for GCSE (9-1) Astronomy*, containing tutorials over 850 worked examples and practice questions, are located inside the rear cover.

Finally, whether you are a student, teacher or merely inquisitive reader, may I wish you every enjoyment and success in your study of GCSE (9-1) Astronomy.

Nigel Marshall, High Peak, Derbyshire, 1st May 2017

1 Planet Earth

1.1 The Earth's structure

It might seem appropriate to begin this Astronomy course with a Geography lesson!

With a mean diameter of 13 000 km, the Earth is the largest of the **terrestrial planets** (the others are Mercury, Venus and Mars). Its polar diameter is slightly smaller than its equatorial diameter (by 42 km), making the Earth's shape that of an **oblate spheroid** (think of sitting on, and squashing, a large beach ball).

Over 70% of the Earth's surface is covered by water. In between the oceans and frozen polar regions, its landforms display a huge diversity of features: mountain ranges, volcanoes, deserts, rainforests, grasslands and glaciers, to name just a few.

The Earth has four major internal divisions:

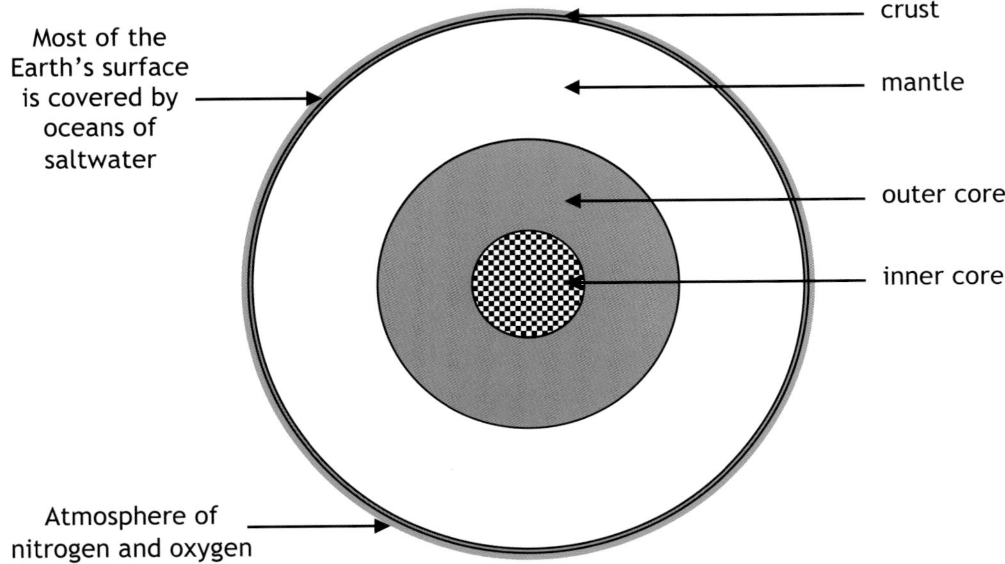

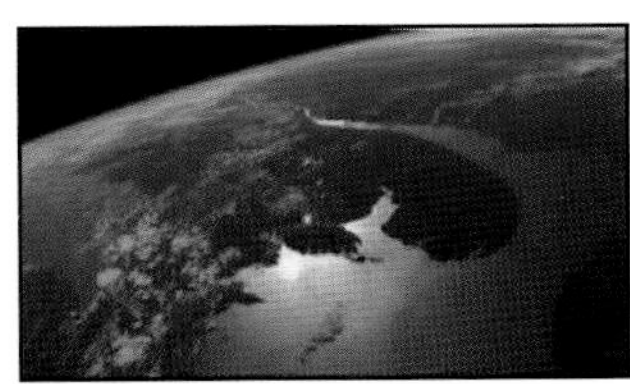

The Gulf of St Lawrence, photographed from the International Space Station.

Image credit: NASA/Astronaut Ron Garan

Japan's tallest peak is Mt. Fuji, an active volcano ~100 km southwest of Tokyo.

Image credit: NASA

The Amazon rainforest in Brazil is slowly being destroyed by deforestation and fires.

Image credit: CIFOR

The Perito Moreno Glacier in Patagonia is one of our planet's more stable glaciers.

Image credit: Etienne Berthier, Université de Toulouse

Relatively speaking, the Earth's solid crust is very thin, ranging in thickness from 0 - 70 km. The older **continental crust** consists of low-density rocks such as granite, and younger, thinner (up to 10 km think) **oceanic crust** consists of darker, denser rocks such as basalt.

The crust is split up into to a number of continent-sized **tectonic plates** that literally float on top of the silicate **mantle.** This extends half-way to the Earth's centre and makes up ~80% of the Earth's volume. The lower mantle is solid whereas the upper mantle is semi-molten, allowing thermal convection currents to rise and fall, driving the sideways motions of the tectonic plates.

The **outer core**, where the temperature is ~5000 K, is made of liquid iron with some nickel. Currents of charged particles that flow in the outer core are responsible for the Earth's magnetic field.

The temperature of the solid **inner core** is ~5500 K - this is about the same temperature as the Sun's photosphere - but the high pressure here prevents the iron and nickel from melting.

1.2 Latitude and longitude

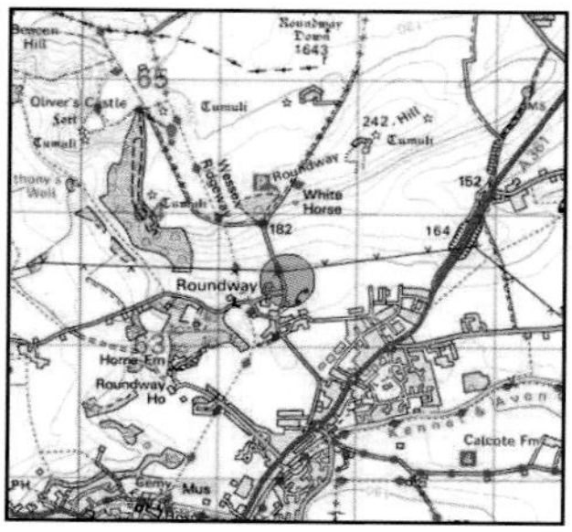

A 4-figure grid reference can be used to locate a general area on an OS map.

Image credit: Ordnance Survey

The network of lines that criss-cross an Ordnance Survey map, a page in an atlas and a 3-dimensional world globe help us to locate a general area (such as using a 4-figure grid reference) or to pinpoint a particular location in terms of its **latitude** and **longitude**.

Although they are drawn on maps as lines, it is important to realise that latitude and longitude are actually angles subtended at the centre of the Earth by imaginary curved lines (arcs) on the Earth's circumference.

On a globe, the grid lines represent latitude and longitude.

Image credit: WordPress.com

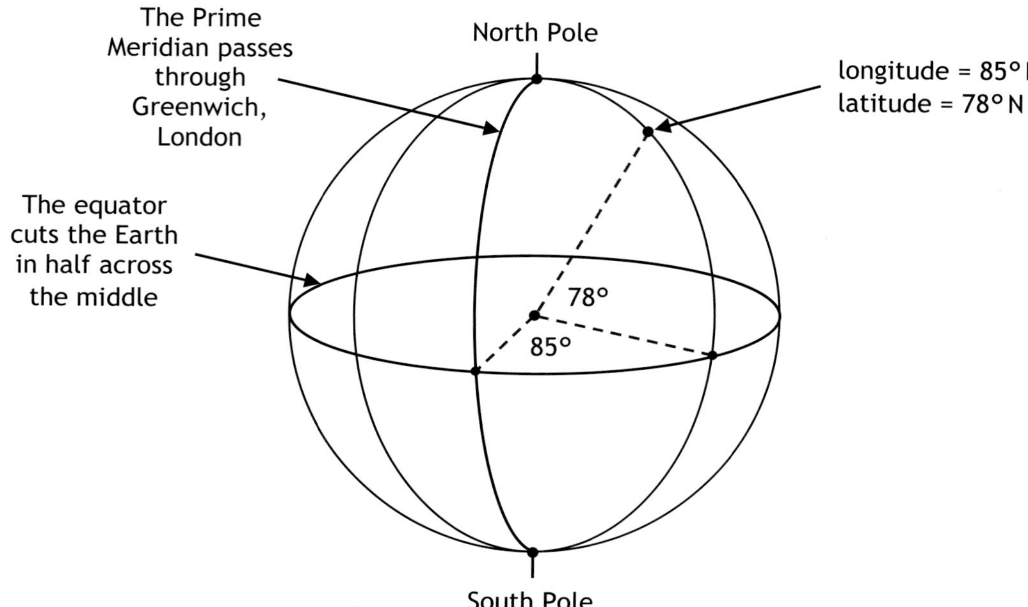

This hotel in Murun in northern Mongolia gets its name from its latitude and longitude: 50° N and 100° E.

Image by the author

Latitude is measured north or south of the Earth's **equator**; this has a latitude of 0° and is an obvious choice for zero. Longitude is measured east or west of the **Prime Meridian**. Until 1884, seafarers used different meridians to define the zero of longitude, but in that year, the International Meridian Conference held in Washington, DC, agreed that *'the meridian passing through...the Observatory of Greenwich should be globally adopted'* as the zero of longitude.

We will now give the Earth its correct 'tilt' in order to introduce some key latitudes that have astronomical significance.

Directions N, S, E and W are just as important as the number of degrees when quoting a location's latitude or longitude: students should ensure these are included.

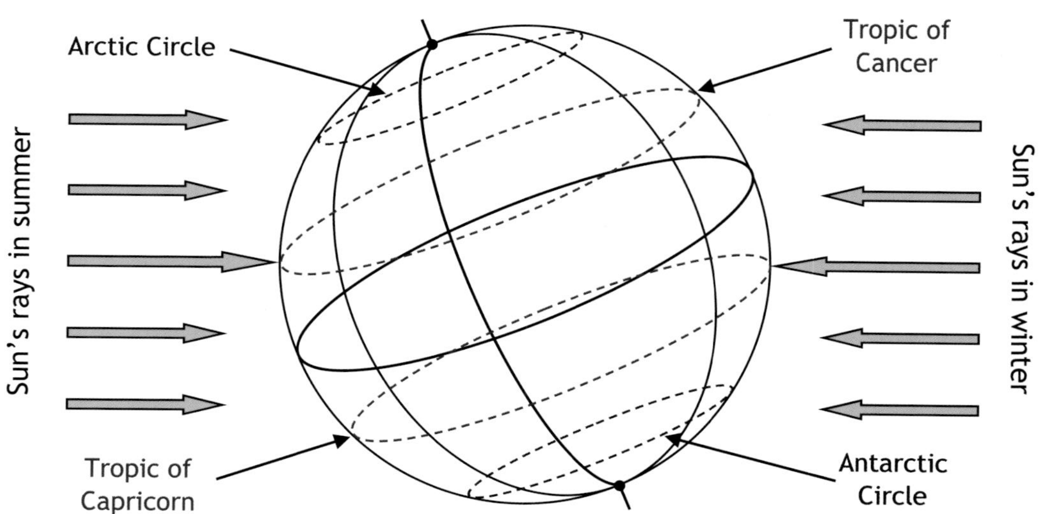

The Earth's polar axis is tilted at 23.5° to the 'vertical'. One consequence is that during its yearly orbit around the Sun, observers at different latitudes on the Earth's surface will 'see' the Sun at different altitudes in the sky.

On or close to March 21st and September 23rd, the Sun lies directly over the equator; these dates correspond to the **spring** and **autumnal equinoxes**.

Midway between, on 21st June and 21st December, the Sun lies directly over the **Tropics of Cancer** (latitude 23.5° N) and **Capricorn** (23.5° S); these dates correspond to the northern hemisphere's **summer** and **winter solstices**.

The 'midnight Sun' as observed from within the Arctic Circle during summer; the Sun neither rises nor sets, giving 24-hours of daylight for several weeks.
Image credit: Norwegian Fjords Cruises

The **Arctic** and **Antarctic Circles** represent the most northern (66.5° N) and southern (66.5° S) latitudes from which the Sun can be seen to rise and set (weather permitting) on every day of the year.

1.3 The Earth's atmosphere

Our atmosphere provides us with oxygen to breathe, absorbs harmful solar UV and X-radiation, regulates our planet's temperature to a mean 15° C and protects us from (most) meteoroid strikes.

Despite these benefits, our atmosphere has several drawbacks for astronomers:

- The sky is blue, making observations restricted to night time. Light is scattered by oxygen and nitrogen molecules in our atmosphere; most scattering occurs at the shortest (blue) wavelengths, and so the sky is predominantly blue;
- Air in the atmosphere is continuously in turbulent motion: different densities of air rise and fall on a variety of scales, causing light to refract and change direction as it passes through the different layers. These adverse **seeing conditions** make the stars appear to 'twinkle'.

Skyglow illuminates the sky, making most stars invisible.
Image credit: Blog.nus/CIT

Another major problem for astronomers is light pollution ('glow and glare'):

- **Skyglow** is the rusty orange haze cast by lights near urban conurbations;
- Local **glare** from sports grounds, supermarket car parks, streetlights and security lights that ruin our eyes' night vision (**dark adaptation**).

Visitors to the Royal Observatory in Greenwich pose for photographs with one foot in the eastern and one in the western hemisphere.

Image by the author

There are plenty of Prime Meridian souvenirs in the Royal Observatory gift shop!

Image by the author

Use an atlas to find the latitudes and longitudes (to the nearest degree) of:

a) Bandung, Indonesia
b) Quingdao, China
c) Minsk, Belarus
d) Lima, Peru

Answers to all after Index

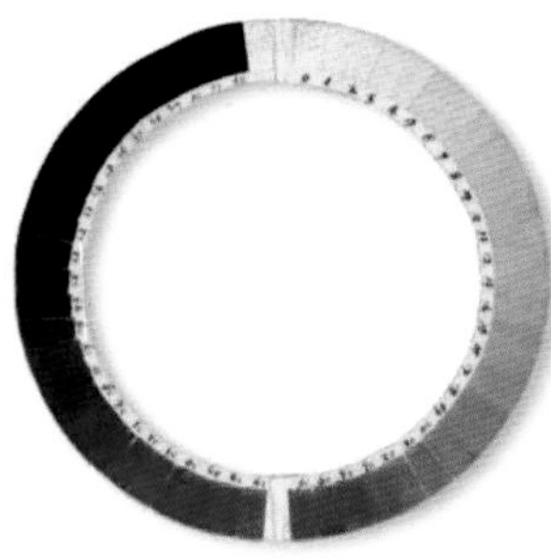

Invented in 1789, the **cyanometer** can be used to determine the 'blueness' of the sky.

Image credit: *Bibliothèque de Genève, Switzerland*

In 2009, the Dark Sky Park in Dumfries & Galloway was the first in the UK to be accredited by the International Dark Skies Association.

For further information on the IDSA and the growing number of dark sky sites in the UK, visit darksky.org

Which one of the following is *not* a popular asterism?

The Summer Triangle
The Lozenge
The 'W'
The Northern Cross
The Merry-go-round at the End of the Pier

Answer after Index

2 Celestial observation

2.1 The night sky

So let's get far away from those annoying sources of light pollution and discover what's out there to see in the night sky with our naked eyes. Where better to start our exploration than the region of sky close to, and including, the constellation of Orion, the Hunter!

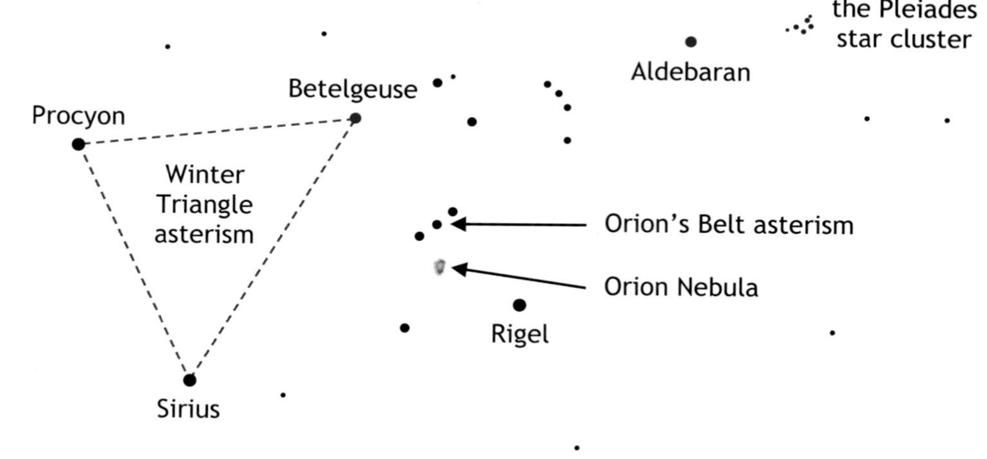

looking south in the winter

The entire sky is split up into 88 different areas called **constellations**. With the exception of just a handful, each contains a pattern of stars that bears no resemblance to the name of the constellation; Orion is one of these exceptions.

In contrast, **asterisms** are unofficial, popular patterns of bright stars that ***do*** have a close likeness to their name; the stars in an asterism might belong to the same or different constellations and include: the Plough (in Ursa Major), Orion's Belt, the 'W' (in Cassiopeia) and the Summer and Winter Triangles.

The Pleiades cluster
Image credit: NASA

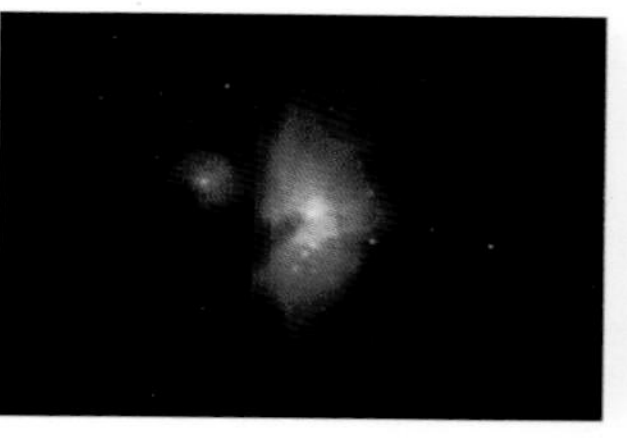

The Orion Nebula
Image credit: Sky-Watching/ A. Welbourn

Comet ISON
Image credit: Waldemar Skorupa/ spaceweather.com

One of Orion's neighbouring constellations, Taurus, the Bull, boasts one of the most beautiful **open clusters** of stars, the Pleiades. Orion itself contains a faint, rather fuzzy pink patch of light just below the Belt. This is a stellar nursery of young stars, gas and dust: the Orion Nebula.

During an observing session, it is likely that an observer might see - probably out of the corner of one eye - a **meteor** or **shooting star**.

This will appear for a split second as a bright streak of light caused by a dust particle, probably from the tail of a comet, burning up in the atmosphere.

Comets themselves are rare visitors to the inner Solar System, but observers might be lucky to spot one as an extended fuzzy object, possibly showing one or two tails, moving slowly against the background stars from night to night.

Even more luck will be needed to observe a **supernova**: only 3 have been observed with the naked eye in our Galaxy in the last 1000 years. A supernova would appear as a bright new star, be visible for possibly a few weeks and then slowly fade, as the time-lapse sequence shows.

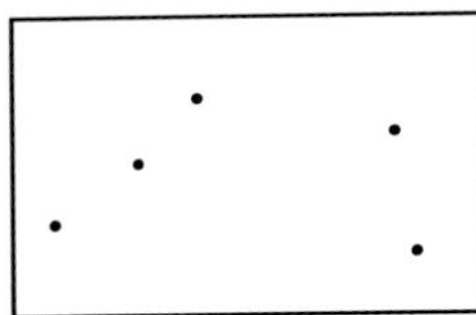

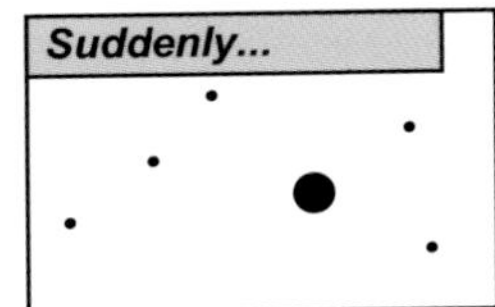

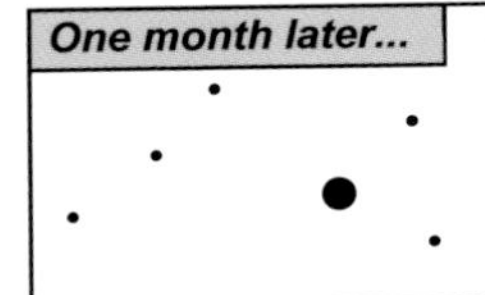

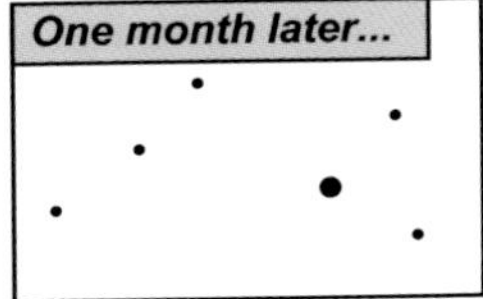

On most evenings it is possible to observe one or more **planets**. Unlike the stars, these do not appear to twinkle as they slowly move eastwards from night to night through an imaginary narrow strip of sky called the **Zodiacal Band**.

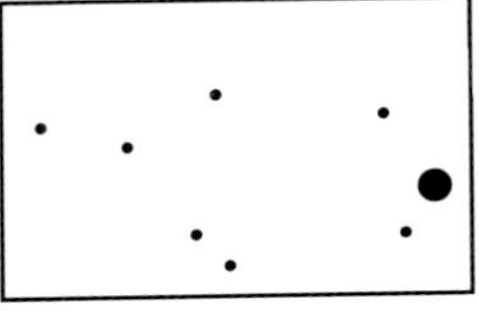

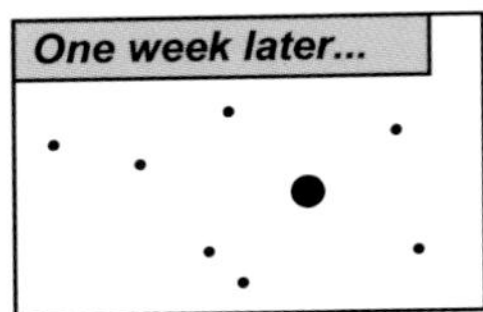

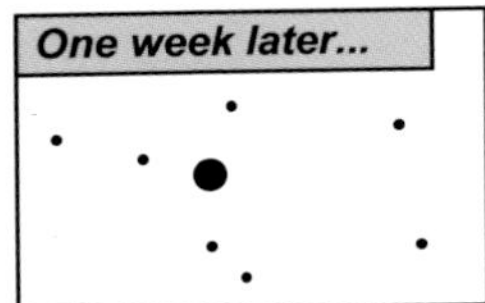

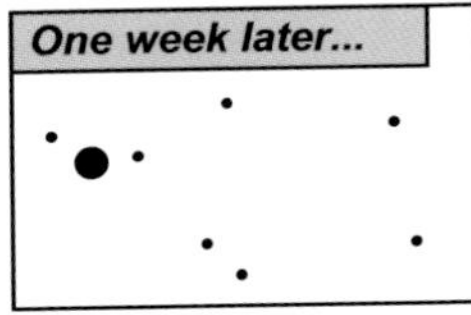

Among the more spectacular astronomical phenomena are the dazzling displays of green, yellow and red curtains and whirlpools of light in the sky, popularly known as the Northern and Southern Lights (or **Aurora Borealis** and **Aurora Australis** respectively). These are only generally visible from polar regions, although they have been observed on rare occasions from mid-UK latitudes.

2.2 Stars and constellations

The diagrams show a selection of the constellations and asterisms that are listed in the GCSE (9-1) Astronomy specification.

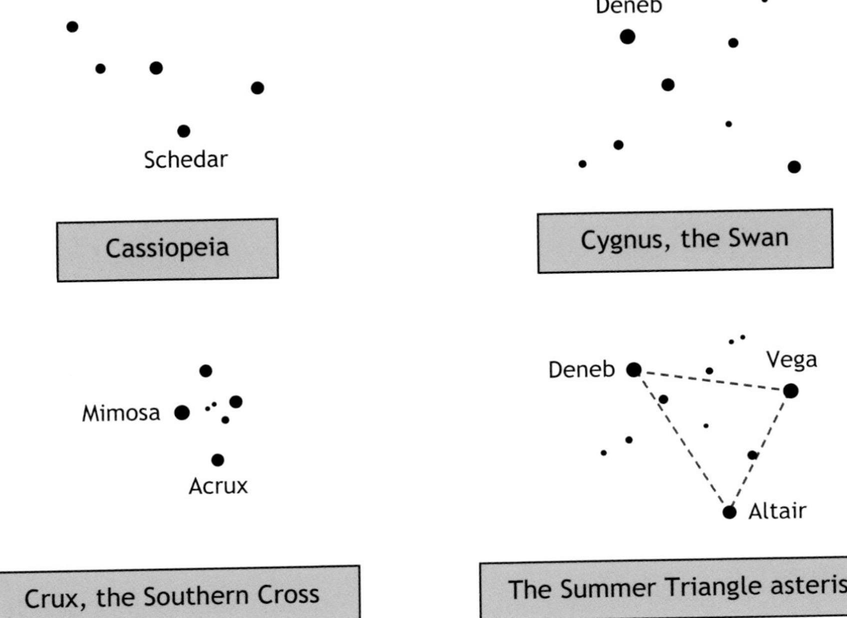

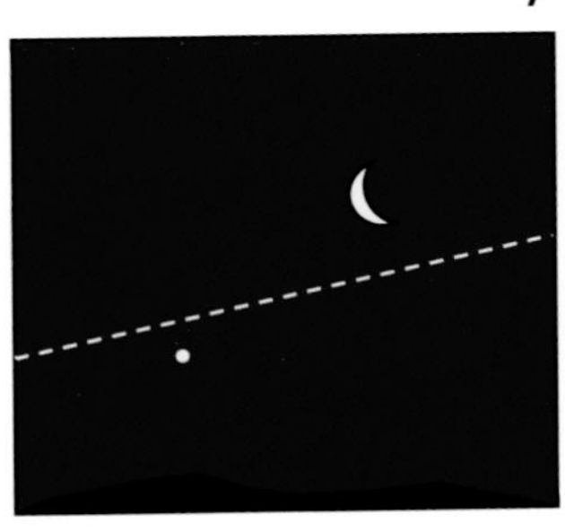

The Moon and Saturn in the pre-dawn sky. The motion of the Moon and the planets is confined to a narrow strip called the **Zodiacal Band** that is centred on the path that the Sun takes during one year: the **ecliptic** (shown dashed).

The *New Pupil Toolkit for GCSE (9-1) Astronomy* contains comprehensive notes on how different cultures named their constellations, asterisms and stars; the notes also describe how the official list of 88 constellations was established by the International Astronomical Union.

The spectacular *Aurora Borealis* (Northern Lights)

Image credit: Nick Russill

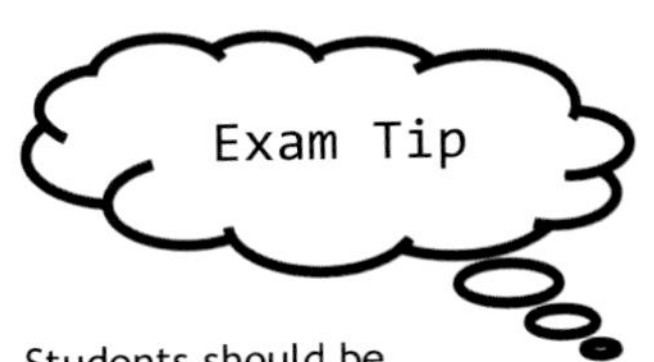

Students should be able to ***recognise*** and ***draw***:

Cassiopeia
Cygnus
Orion
The Plough
Crux, the Southern Cross
The Summer Triangle
The Great Square of Pegasus

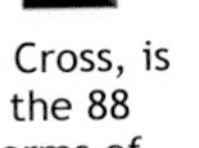

Crux, the Southern Cross, is the ***smallest*** of all the 88 constellations (in terms of area) and yet it appears on ***five*** national flags.

Stellarium is a superb and easy-to-use piece of planetarium software for your computer that shows a realistic sky with constellation artwork. It can be downloaded free of charge from:

www.stellarium.org

Another very useful piece of software is *Heavens Above*, which asks you to enter your geographic location. In return, it will tell you when and where in the sky artificial satellites (including the International Space Station) will be visible:

www.heavens-above.com

We found this superb celestial sphere complete with a model Earth among many other educational maps and globes for sale in the US (with international checkout facilities) at:

www.ultimateglobes.com

This student is using the *Essential Maths Skills for GCSE (9-1) Astronomy* CD-ROM to help her to get to grips with the celestial sphere and other mathematical topics.

Many asterisms contain stars that act as **pointers** to specific objects in the sky.

For example, the three stars in Orion's Belt point downwards to the bright star Sirius and upwards, not only to the bright red star Aldebaran, but also beyond to the Pleiades cluster. Two further examples are shown below.

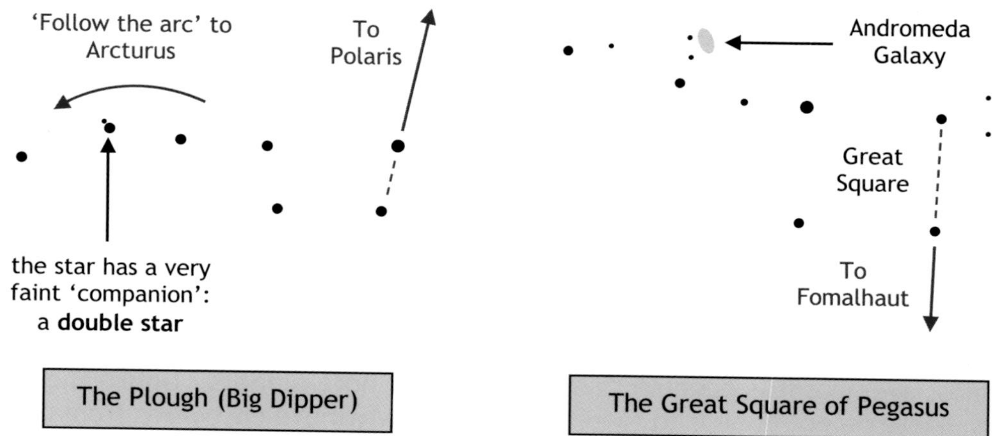

In addition to its stars pointing out the bright star Arcturus and the pole star Polaris, the Plough also contains a fine example of an optical **double star** (two stars, physically unrelated, that happen to lie roughly in the line of sight).

The Great Square of Pegasus is a good starting point for observing the **Andromeda Galaxy** - this is the most distant object that can be seen with the naked eye - which is visible as a very faint, fuzzy patch of dim light.

Concluding our tour, keen observers might see an **artificial satellite**, most of which move slowly from north to south as reasonably bright points of light in the twilight sky before fading from view as they enter the Earth's shadow.

These should not be confused with **aircraft** that are easily identified from green and red right-of-way 'navigation' lights and flashing white identification lights - it's likely that the aircraft engines will be heard too!

2.3 The celestial sphere

Having introduced the latitude and longitude system for points on the Earth's surface in Chapter 1, we now turn our attention to a similar network of lines that are used to map stars and other objects in the sky (or more correctly, on an imaginary sphere concentric with the Earth: the **celestial sphere**).

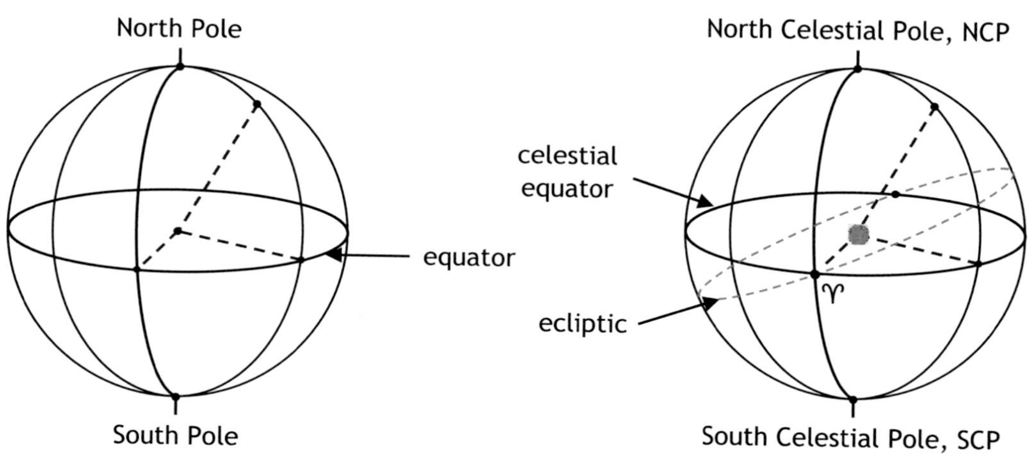

In terms of its poles and equator, the celestial sphere should have some degree of familiarity. However, there is no obvious celestial equivalent of the Prime Meridian (which marks the zero of longitude), and so we have added:

- the path taken by the Sun on the celestial sphere during one year (the **ecliptic**, shown in orange);
- the point where the ecliptic cuts the celestial equator on its 'journey' from south to north (the **First Point of Aries**, denoted by ♈).

2.4 Coordinate systems

'Imagine wrapping a huge sheet of graph paper around two back-to-back pudding basins.' **anon.**

Most astronomers use the **equatorial coordinate system** in which the celestial equivalents of our latitude and longitude are **declination** (*abbr.* dec or δ) and **right ascension** (RA or α):

- Declination is simply the projection of latitude onto the celestial sphere; it is measured in degrees (+ and - signs indicate N and S);
- Right ascension is measured eastwards from the First Point of Aries; it is measured in hours and minutes (*abbr.* h and min) where 1 h ≡ 15°, and just like time intervals, there are 60 min in 1 hour (so 1 min ≡ 0.25°).

Let's now unwrap our 'huge sheet of graph paper' to reveal two star charts.

declination

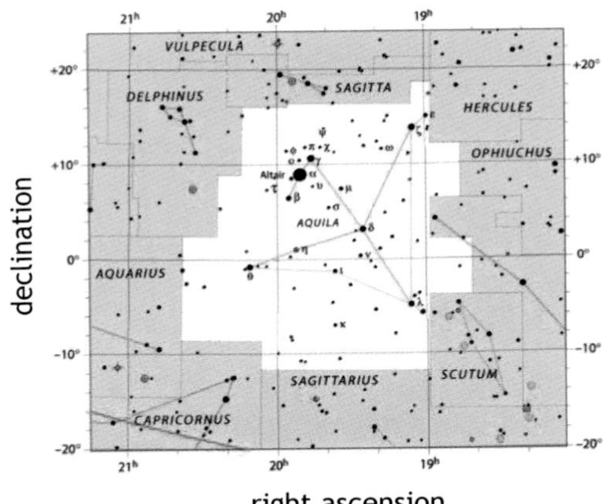

right ascension

declination

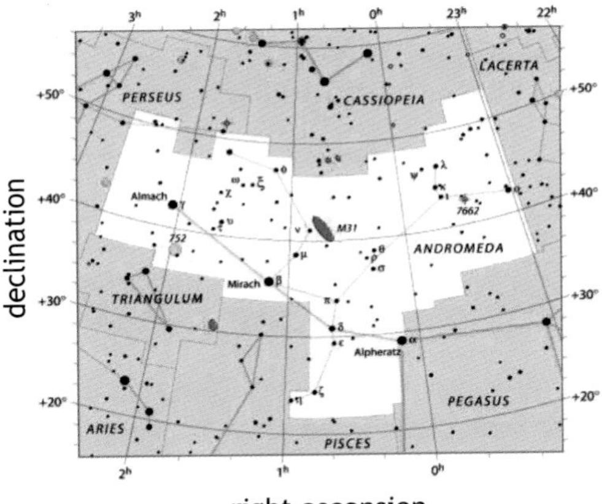

right ascension

Notice that close to the celestial equator, the RA lines are (almost) parallel to each other- see chart on left, courtesy of *Sky & Telescope* magazine - but close to the poles, the lines converge (like lines of longitude on maps of the world).

Note also that since we are now 'inside' the celestial sphere looking 'outwards' to the sky, right ascension increases ***to the left***.

Many amateur astronomers use a much more observer-friendly **horizontal coordinate system** involving **azimuth** and **altitude**.

Azimuth is simple a bearing (measured in degrees) from due north - that's geographical, not magnetic - moving round eastwards to the point on the observer's horizon directly under the star; it ranges from 0° to 360° (0° again).

Altitude is then found by the angle from the observer's horizon upwards to the star or other celestial object; it ranges from 0° to 90° (the observer's **zenith**).

On or around March 21st (the spring equinox), the Sun slowly moves from south to north across the celestial equator; the First Point of Aries (♈) marks the zero of right ascension.

Image by the author

RA = 5 h 30 min
dec = +78°

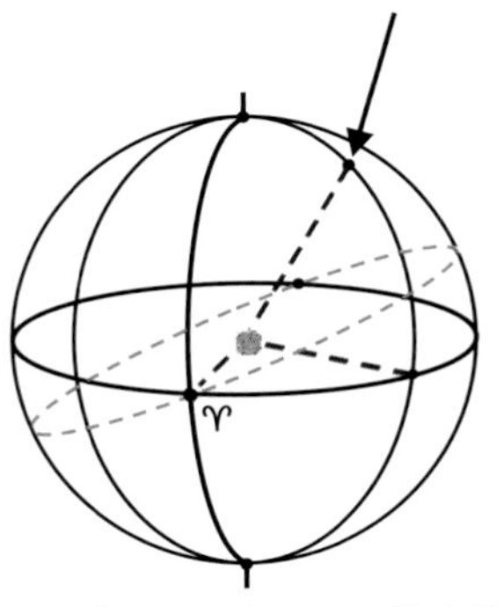

The diagram shows us that the 'star' would have a right ascension of around 5 h 30 min and a declination of +78°.

1. Which star is closest to the North Celestial Pole?

2. Use a star chart to find the equatorial coordinates of these stars:

a) Sirius
b) Betelgeuse
c) Fomalhaut
d) Deneb

Answers after Index

Azimuth can be given simply as a cardinal point (N, E, S, W) or even an intercardinal point (NE, SW etc.)

There are plenty of worked examples and practice questions on equatorial and horizontal coordinates, local sidereal time and hour angle in the *Essential Maths Skills for GCSE (9-1) Astronomy* CD-ROM available directly from Mickledore Publishing.

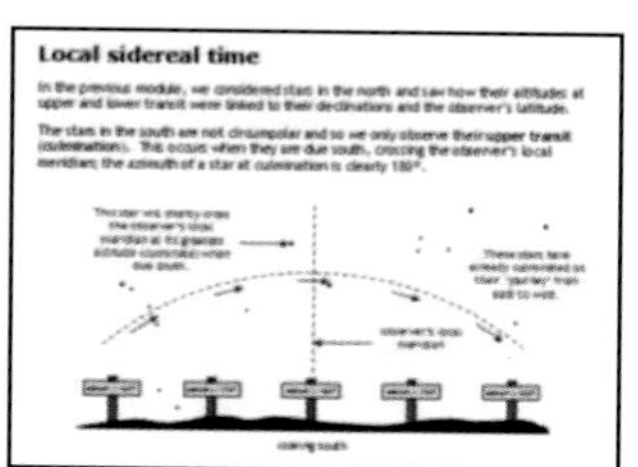

1. An astronomer observes a star with RA = 05 h 35 min crossing her meridian.
   What is the astronomer's LST?
2. For an observer, the hour angle of Sirius is -0 h 45 min.
   In how many minutes' time will Sirius be due south?
3. In the observatory of the Frozentoze Astronomical Society, LST is 04:15.
   How long must elapse before a star of RA = 03 h 45 min crosses the observatory's meridian?

Answers after Index

Aided Observational Task B12 involves taking long-exposure photographs of the area of sky around the NCP to determine the length of one sidereal day.

All students need is a camera that will shoot a time-lapse exposure of about 3 hours (with the aperture as small as possible), a sturdy tripod to hold the camera steady, a printer to obtain a large image that can be drawn on, a ruler and a protractor.

2.5 Diurnal motion

Like the Sun, the stars rise in the east, reach their highest point (**culminate**) when they are due south as they cross the observer's **meridian**, and later set in the west. This apparent motion of the stars is called **diurnal motion** and it is simply a result of the Earth rotating on its polar axis from west to east.

With respect to the stars, the Earth rotates through 360° in 23 h 56 min; this is one **sidereal day**. However, during this time, the Earth has moved around the Sun by about 1°, and so needs to rotate for a further 4 min to align a given point on its surface with the Sun once again. 24 h 0 min ≡ one **solar day**. It follows that the stars rise, culminate and set 4 min earlier (GMT) each day.

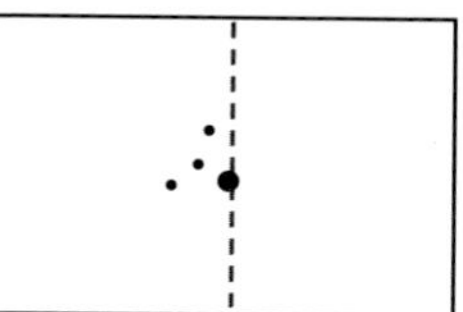
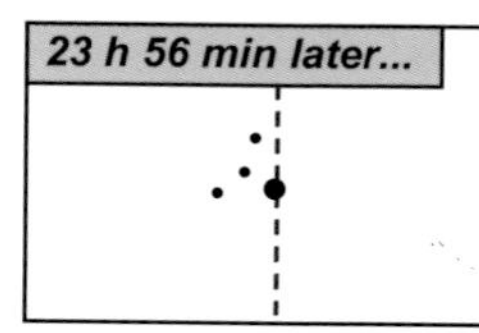

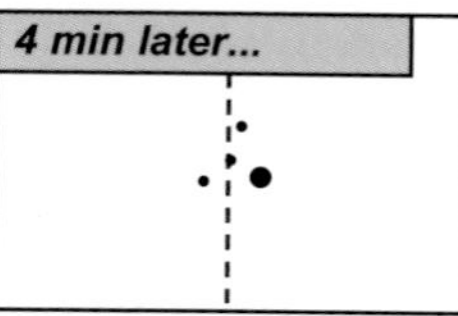

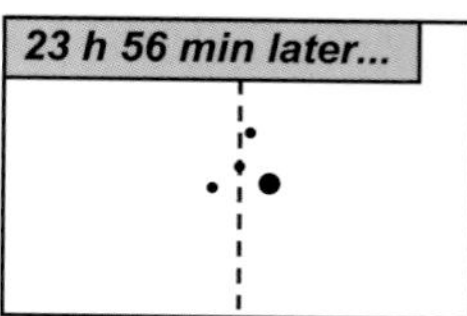

Time sequence showing a group of stars crossing the observer's meridian (the imaginary N - S line shown in dashed blue that also runs through the zenith) in the south.

Most astronomers observe the stars as opposed to the Sun, and so astronomers use clocks based on **local sidereal time** (LST) rather than clock time.

The local sidereal time of an observer is the right ascension of a star that lies on the observer's meridian at a given moment in time. This means that if a star with RA = 14 h 45 min lies on an observer's meridian, the LST is 14:45.

Observers often make use of a star's **hour angle**; this is the time (in hours and min) since the object was last crossing the observer's meridian. It follows that:

hour angle = local sidereal time - right ascension

If the hour angle is negative, its value tells an astronomer how much time must elapse before the star or other celestial object will be crossing his or her meridian (the best time to observe it) - a bit like waiting for a bus!

Turning our attention northwards, the stars appear to revolve around the NCP in an anticlockwise sense, from west to east 'below' Polaris, and east to west 'above' Polaris.

Polaris, v. close to NCP

One complete revolution takes 23 h 56 min (one **sidereal day**).

Stars in the north, including those in the Plough, appear to revolve around the NCP (which is v. close to Polaris) in an anticlockwise sense.

west of north   north   east of north

Using simple geometry, it can be shown that:

altitude of NCP (or SCP) = observer's latitude

Since Polaris is only 0.5° from the NCP, then to a good approximation:

altitude of Polaris = observer's latitude

A useful angular measure for astronomers is a star's **polar distance** (sometimes called **co-declination**). This is the angular distance of a star from the NCP. Since the declination of the NCP is +90°, it follows that:

polar distance = 90° - declination

Each small circle that a star traces out during one sidereal day has a radius equal to its polar distance (as indicated by the double arrows).

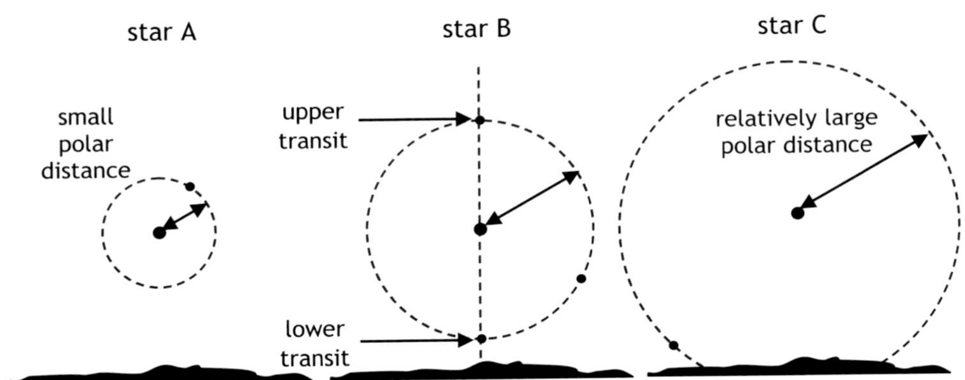

For star B, we have shown the observer's meridian. The points at which a star crosses the local meridian are called **upper transit** and **lower transit**, and the altitudes of a star at these two points allow us to link its equatorial and horizontal coordinates:

altitude = latitude ± polar distance
at upper and lower transits

Note that the upper transit is also the point at which a star **culminates**.

2.6 Circumpolar stars

In the diagrams above, the polar distances of stars A and B are so small that these stars do not set and remain 'visible' all the time - these are called **circumpolar stars**. Star C, however, has a larger polar distance and is due to set below the northern horizon before rising again; it is ***not*** circumpolar.

For a star to be circumpolar, its polar distance must be less than the altitude of the NCP (which is equal to the latitude of the observer). Since polar distance = 90° - declination, then for a star to be circumpolar:

90° - declination < latitude of observer

So, for example, the star Thuban (declination +64°) ***will*** be circumpolar from Ulaanbaatar (latitude 48°N) because 90° - 64° (= 26°) < 48°.

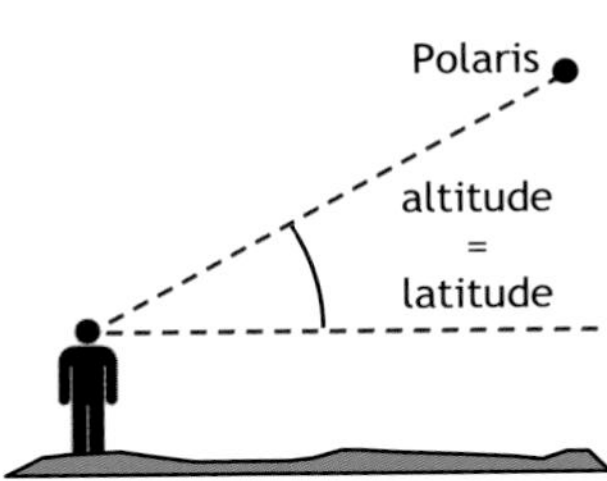

Looking from the east, the altitude of Polaris (actually the NCP) above the northern horizon is equal to the observer's latitude. This has always been an important navigational aid for seafarers and desert travellers.

1. Calculate the polar distances for the following stars:

a) Capella (dec = +46°)
b) Dubhe (dec = +62°)
c) Vega (dec = +39°)
d) Acrux (dec = -63°)

2. True or False?

a) The larger the declination of a star, the smaller its polar distance.

b) The larger the declination of a star, the greater the chance of it being circumpolar.

Answers after Index

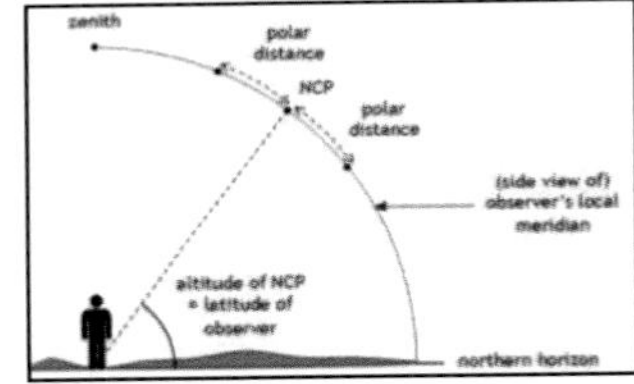

This extract, from the *Essential Maths Skills* CD-ROM, shows how polar distance links latitude with altitude.

This amazing time-lapse photograph of the southern sky above Mt. Broma in Indonesia shows that some stars are circumpolar whereas others (most of them in this image) are not.

Image credit: Elia Locardi via AndroidGuys.

2.7 Naked-eye observing

Astronomers don't necessarily need specialised equipment when observing the night sky. Indeed, large constellations, the full span of the Milky Way, Earth-orbiting artificial satellites and spectacular meteor showers are perfect 'targets' for naked-eye observers.

The best time to observe celestial objects is when close to culmination: they are highest in the sky and at their brightest. This allows the colours of (some) stars to be detected and more detail to be resolved in 'extended' objects such as nebulae and star clusters. Information on rising and setting times should enable observers to estimate the 'half-way' time at which objects culminate.

Planisphere and star charts, such as those published in *Astronomy Now* and *BBC Sky at Night* magazines are an ideal way of learning what's what and where in the night sky.

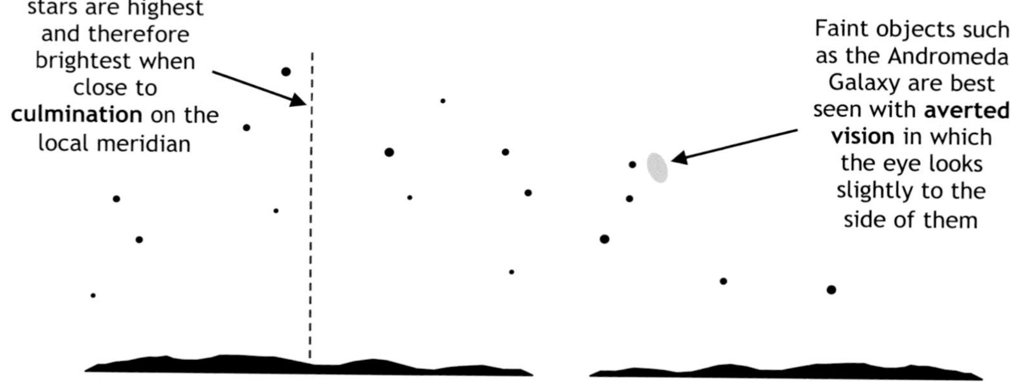

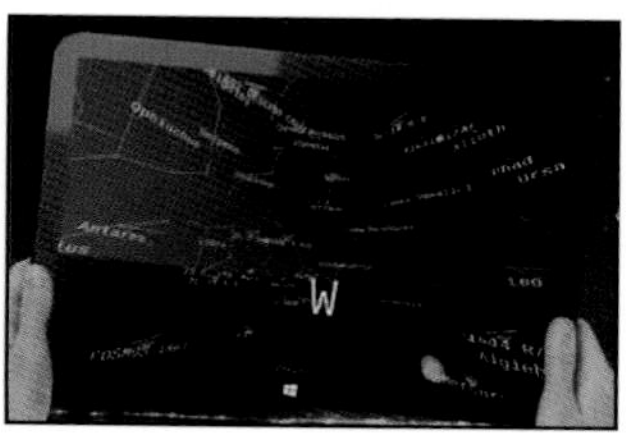

The variety of free apps now available for smartphones is increasing weekly; they are quick and easy to use, but don't expect to see ***all*** the stars displayed on the screen.

It's advisable to choose an app that has a 'night vision' mode so that you won't lose dark adaptation looking at the bright screen.

Before any serious observing can be carried out, the eyes must become fully **dark adapted**; this takes about 20 - 30 minutes of darkness. The retina of the eye contains two types of photoreceptive cell: **rods** (which are not colour-sensitive) and **cones** (which are). The rods are very sensitive to changes in light intensity and are over-sensitised in daylight; they are ideal for night vision, but require time to 'adapt' to low light levels.

A torch should be fitted with a red filter since red light does not destroy the eyes' dark-adapted state.

If a star or nebula is insufficiently bright to stimulate the cones, it will not be seen if looked at directly. The reason for this is that cones are not activated in dim light. It is therefore necessary to stimulate the rods, but these are located on the outside of the optical axis; **averted vision** (looking slightly to the side of the object) allows its light to fall onto the rods and the object to be 'seen'.

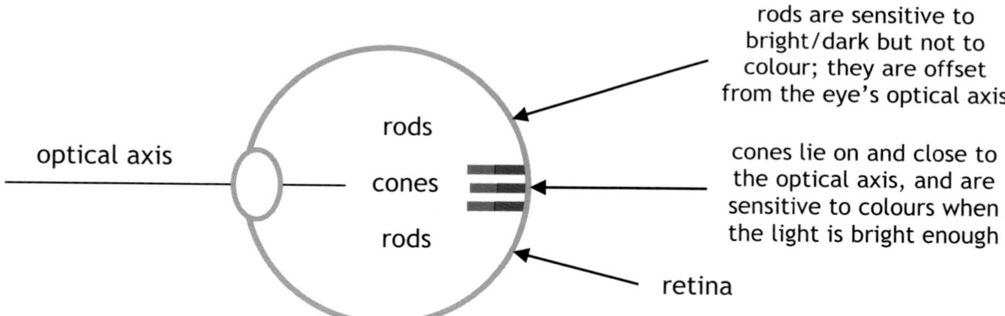

Multi-layered clothing, hats, scarves, gloves and maybe a flask of hot chocolate are a must for observing on those cold winter nights.

Other factors that may affect the visibility of objects in the night sky include the landscape (trees and high buildings tend to block the view), the presence of cloud (even patchy cloud is not very desirable), amount of **light pollution** (both skyglow and local glare), the **transparency** of the atmosphere (recent rain removes dust particles) and the **seeing conditions** relating to the 'steadiness' of the atmosphere, which can be quantified using the I - V **Antoniadi Scale**.

3 The lunar disc

3.1 Surface features of the Moon

Most people are surprised when they learn that out of the Earth, Moon and Sun, it is the Sun that is the most spherical in shape.

In Chapter 1 we saw that the Earth's polar diameter is smaller than its equatorial diameter by 42 km, making its mean diameter ~ 13 000 km.

For the Moon, the difference is only 4 km compared with its mean diameter of 3500 km. So like the Earth, the shape of the Moon is also an **oblate spheroid**.

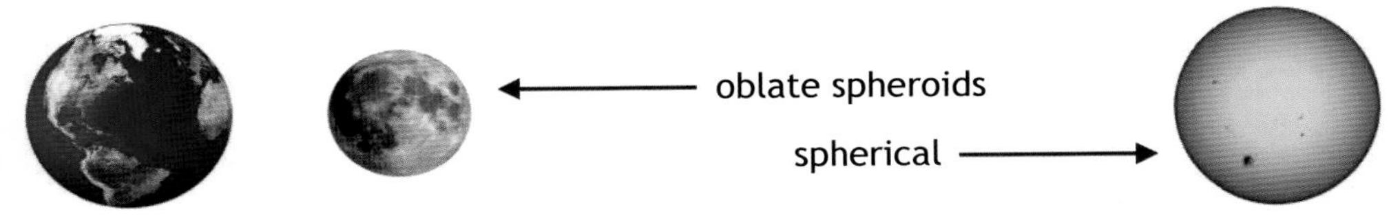

A 10 km difference for the Sun is insignificant compared with its mean diameter of 1.4 million km; the Sun is almost perfectly spherical.

Even though the full disc of the Moon subtends an angle of only 0.5° at the human eye, on clear nights and with perfect seeing conditions, many features of the Moon are discernable without resorting to the use of optical aids.

To the relative newcomer, the first contrasting features to notice are the large dark-grey, relatively smooth **seas** (Latin: *maria*, singular *mare* - pronounced 'mah-ray') of volcanic basalt rock and lighter-grey, mountainous, highly-cratered **highlands** (*terrae*, sing. *terra*) of igneous rock called anorthosite. Further scrutiny reveals numerous craters, mountain ranges and valleys.

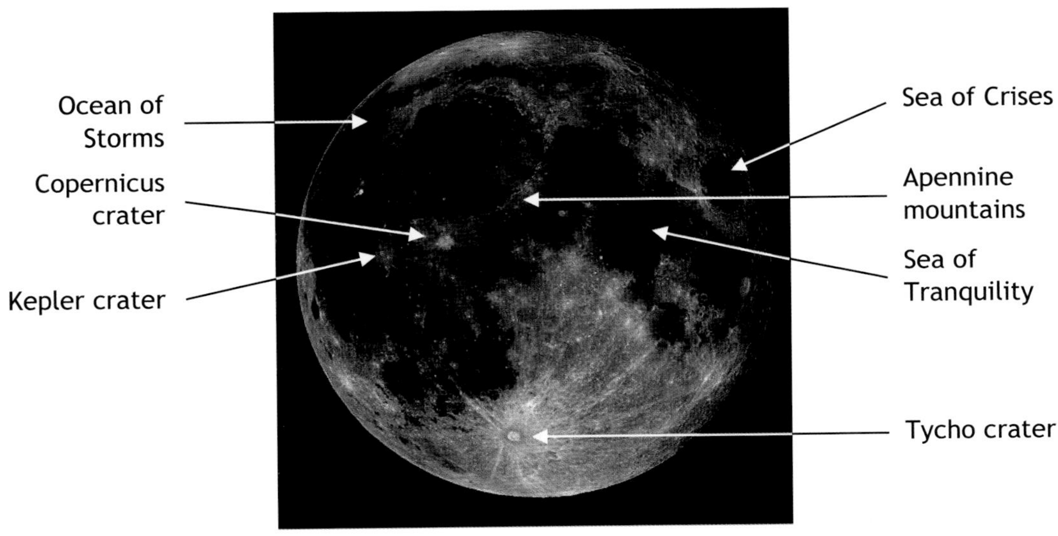

The principal lunar features that students may be asked to identify are shown in the diagram above. Most are visible to the naked eye, but binoculars or a small telescope will resolve these in much more detail.

In contrast, the Moon's far side is almost devoid of *maria* (see page 15).

True or False?

a) The Moon is 100 times closer to us than Venus.

b) Half of the Moon's surface is in permanent darkness.

c) Lunar 'seas' are covered in water.

d) During a 'supermoon', the lunar disc appears larger because the Moon is slightly closer to the Earth than usual.

Answers after Index

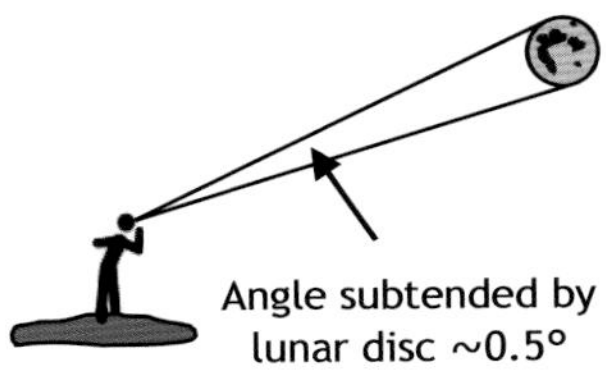

The full disc of the Moon subtends an angle of just less than 0.5°, and yet even the casual observer can pick out seas, highlands, large craters and (possibly) mountains and valleys.

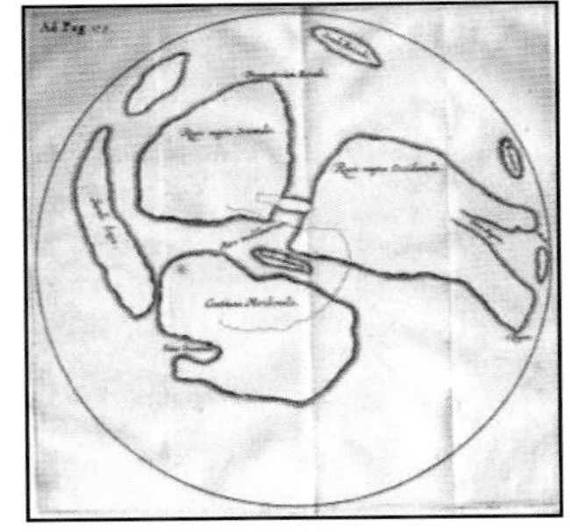

One of the earliest (c.1600) naked-eye sketches of the lunar disc was made by English physicist William Gilbert (better known for his contribution to our understanding of magnetism). *Image credit: Sky & Telescope magazine*

Among the numerous *YouTube* clips about the Moon, this is considered (by the author) to be one of the best.

If you can keep up with its fast-flowing format, it explains a wealth of topics including how lunar *maria* and craters were formed, why the Moon looks bigger than usual when rising or setting, and the implications of discovering water on the Moon.

www.youtube.com/watch?v=mCzchPx3yF8

Another *YouTube* clip, this time from *NASA*, shows how to make realistic craters to help students to understand their structure and formation.

www.youtube.com/watch?v=HTukFx17Ryg

1. How many days does it take the Moon to rotate through an angle of 120°?
2. How many astronauts have walked on the Moon?

Answers after Index

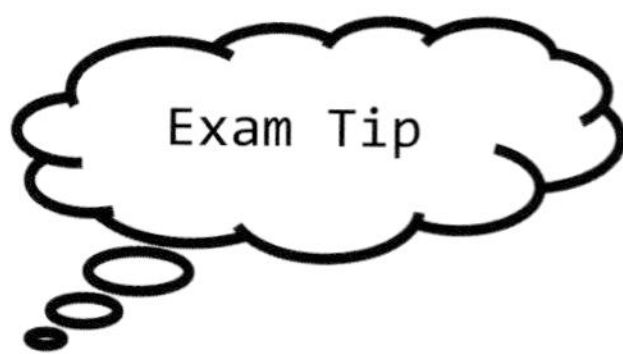

All students should read examination questions ***carefully*** to make sure that they understand their requirements.

It is quite easy to confuse ***sidereal*** months (27.3 days) with ***solar*** months (29.5 days).

Early in the Moon's history, probably while still cooling and forming a primitive crust, its surface was bombarded heavily by left-over rocky debris - large meteoroids and asteroids - from the formation of the Solar System. This bombardment carved out the Moon's cratered highlands and *mare* basins.

About 4000 million years ago, the storm of debris abated and molten lava was able to seep through the relatively-thin nearside crust where it solidified and formed the lunar *maria*; mountain ranges were thrust upwards near the edges of the *maria*, creating deep valleys in between mountains.

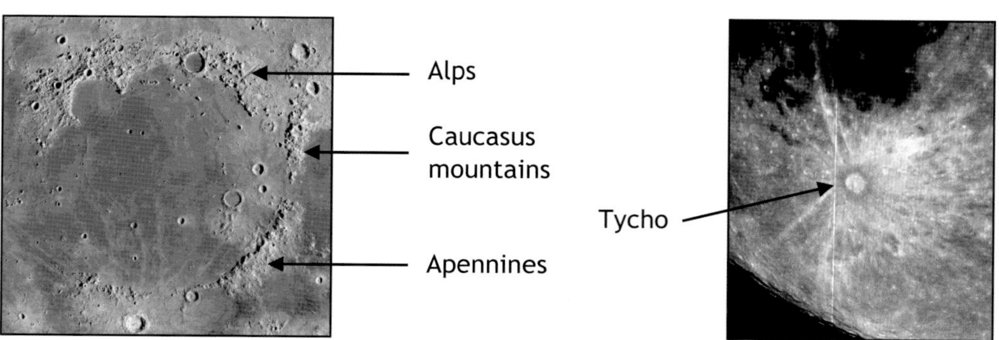

Left: The Sea of Rains (*Mare Imbrium*) is enclosed on most sides by mountain ranges, including the Apennines. Right: The rayed-crater Tycho, the result of a huge impact.

Lunar craters were formed by meteoroids striking the lunar surface. Each impact caused a shockwave that compressed the surface material to leave a large cavity. The subsequent 'rebound' splattered material - this is known as **ejecta** - out in all directions, creating the bright streaks that we see as **rays**.

3.2 The Moon's orbit

The Moon revolves around the Earth once in 27.3 days; this is also the time taken for the Moon to rotate on its axis by 360°.

This is no fluke! Most large moons of the giant planets also show **synchronous rotation**. This arises from internal **tidal gravitational forces** slowing down the moons' periods of rotation until these become **tidally locked** (equal) to their orbital periods (this will be explained in chapter 12).

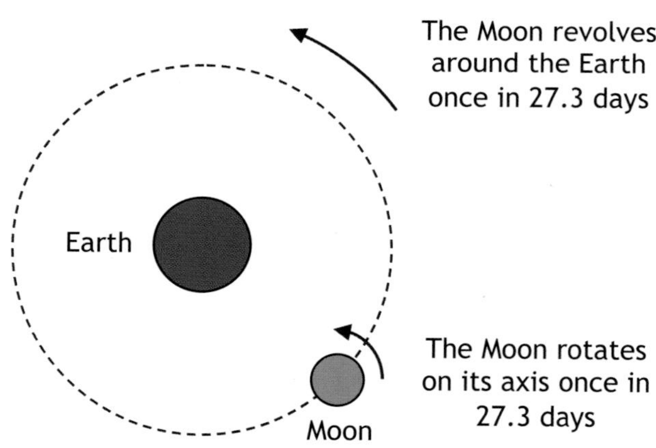

The Moon's orbital period of 27.3 days is known as one **sidereal month**. It should not be confused with a **synodic** or **solar month** (the time interval from one full Moon to the next) which is 29.5 days (see chapter 11).

Although the Moon is in a synchronous orbit and only shows us its **near side**, over a period of time it is actually possible to observe up to 59% of the Moon's surface from Earth due to various kinds of **lunar libration**.

The Moon does physically wobble a little, and it is also possible to see 'under and over' the Moon's polar regions from low and high latitudes on Earth. In addition, observers can peek around the edges of the Moon's eastern and western limbs when seen from different viewpoints at moonrise and moonset.

However, most libration is due to whereabouts the Moon is placed in its orbit.

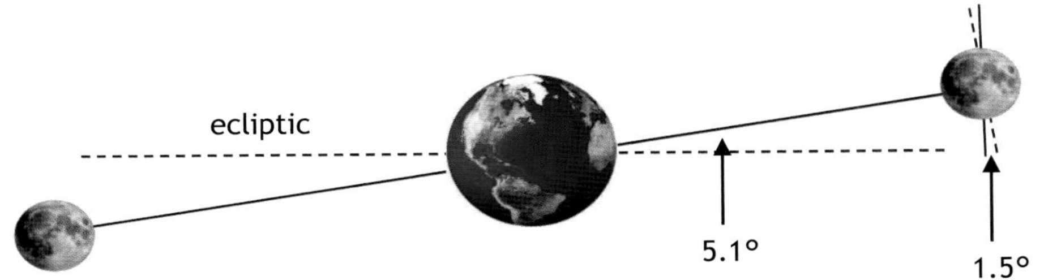

The Moon's equator is inclined to the plane of its orbit around the Earth by 1.5°, and the plane of the Moon's orbit it inclined at 5.1° to the ecliptic; this combination makes the Moon appear very high in the sky on occasions and results in a **libration in latitude**.

Consequently, from our vantage point on Earth, we can see 'under' the Moon's south polar region and 'above' the Moon's north polar region to different extents (except twice a month when the Moon is crossing the plane of the Earth's orbit).

Libration in longitude arises from the Moon's varying speed in its elliptical orbit around the Earth. Let's modify the diagram on the opposite page to exaggerate this elliptical nature and show the Moon at weekly intervals.

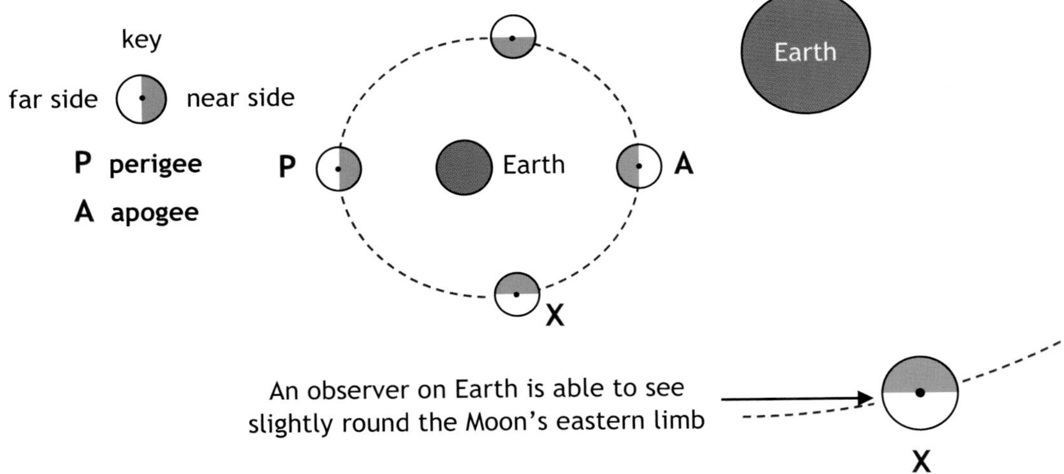

'If you watch a speeded-up movie of the Moon's phase cycle, you will see the Moon saying 'Yes' (nodding) and 'No' (shaking its head) at the same time.'

anon.

There are many such movie clips available on the internet. Try this one on *YouTube*:

https://www.youtube.com/watch?v=3f_21N3wcX8

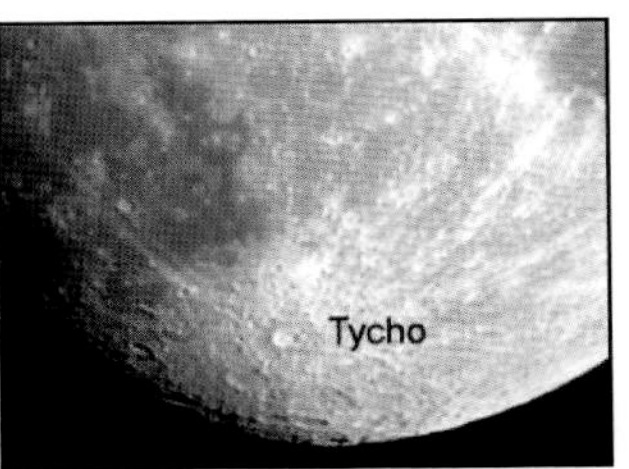

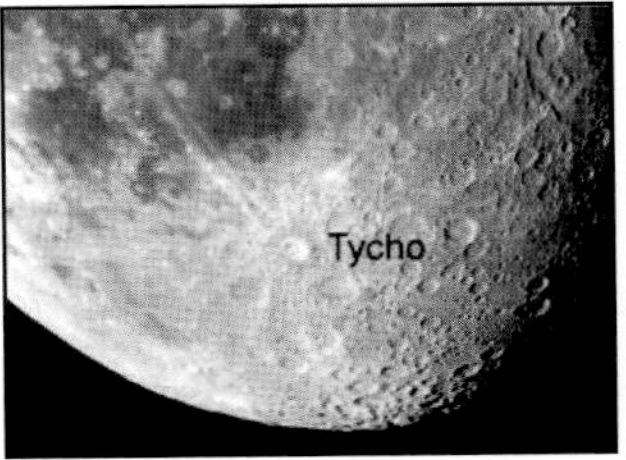

The two images of Tycho crater demonstrate the libration in latitude: much more of the southern polar region below Tycho is visible in the lower image (taken at a time when the Moon appeared much higher in the sky).

Image credits: John Chumack and Frank Barrett via EarthSky News

In accordance with Kepler's second law (see chapter 8), the Moon takes the same time to travel in its orbit from **P** to **X** as it does from **X** to **A**. The Moon's rotation rate, however, remains constant, and so when the Moon is at position **X**, keen observers on Earth will see a little more around its eastern limb. The same will occur when the Moon is travelling away from apogee, allowing observers to glimpse around its western limb.

It should be stressed that all libration effects occur close to the Moon's limbs and so are difficult to observe in detail: we are effectively seeing these extra parts of the lunar surface 'side-on'.

4 Exploring the Moon

4.1 Exploration of the Moon

With some exaggeration of the thickness of the lunar crust, we have drawn the Moon and Earth to the same size in order to compare their internal divisions.

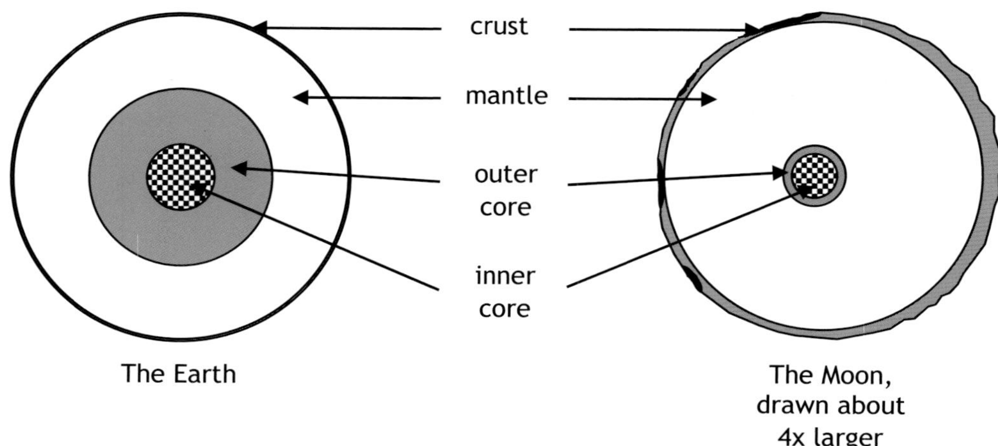

Although the Moon has a crust, mantle and core (inner and outer) like the Earth, there are some notable differences:

- The mean thickness of the lunar crust is 50 - 60 km, typically about 3 times that of the Earth's crust - the thickness in the lunar highlands on the far side can be as large as 160 km - and possibly explains why lunar *maria* are almost exclusively found on the Moon's thinner near side;
- The radius of the Moon's core is less than 25% of the Moon's radius (on Earth the core extends to more than 50% of its radius);
- The Moon's core is not at the physical centre of the Moon but offset by about 2 km towards the near side, i.e. towards Earth.

Prior to 1959, the appearance of the Moon's far side was unknown. In that year, the unmanned Soviet spacecraft *Luna 3* successfully flew around the far side of the Moon. The spacecraft was fitted with a dual-lens camera that took several photographs of the far side; the film was processed on-board, scanned and then transmitted back to Earth once *Luna 3* was close enough.

The images showed the Moon's far side to consist of heavily-cratered highlands.

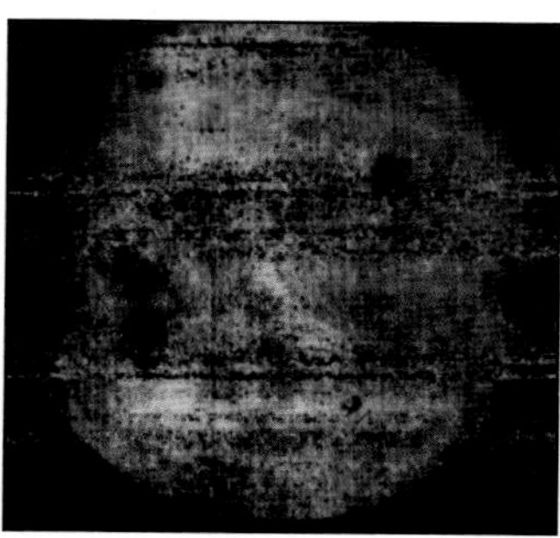

A grainy *Luna 3* image of the Moon's far side showing a lack of *maria*.

The Moon's far side is almost completely covered by highlands.

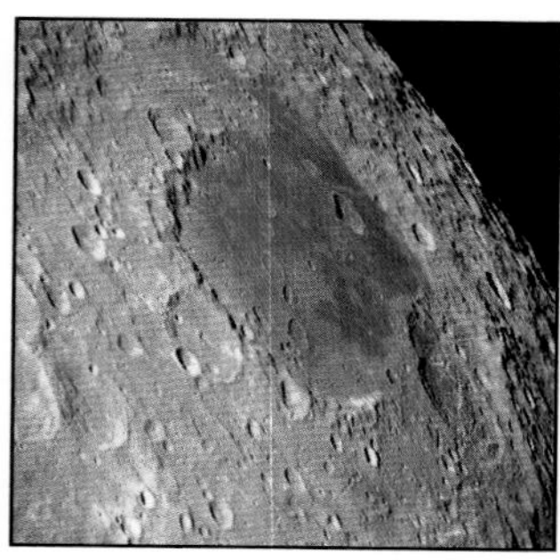

A close-up of the far side's only noteworthy sea, *Mare Moscoviense*

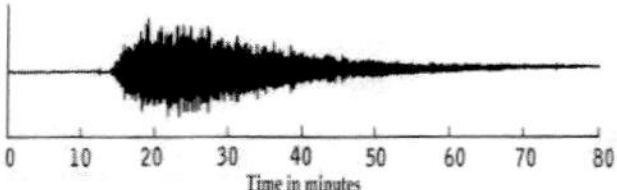

Seismometers were deployed on the surface of the Moon by *Apollo* astronauts in order to detect natural and artificial (by deliberately crashing the *Saturn V* rockets' third stages) moonquakes; the data enabled scientists to study the internal structure of the Moon.

Image credit: NASA

A life-size model of the *Luna 3* spacecraft at the Memorial Museum of Cosmonauts in Moscow. In 1959, *Luna 3* was the first spacecraft to photograph the Moon's far side, showing a significant lack of *maria* in what was otherwise heavily-cratered lunar highlands.

Image by the author

You can find out lots more about the Moon's interior and lunar geology by visiting the *Windows to the Universe* website:

http://www.windows2universe.org/earth/moon/lunar_interior_structure.html

In May 1961, largely in response to the then-Soviet Union's apparent supremacy in space, US President John F. Kennedy made a historic speech to a joint session of Congress in which he announced the ambitious *Apollo* space programme of landing men on the Moon and returning them safely back to Earth 'before this decade [the 1960s] is out'.

US President John F. Kennedy addressing the special joint session of Congress in 1961.

The giant *Saturn V* rocket blasts off from Cape Kennedy.

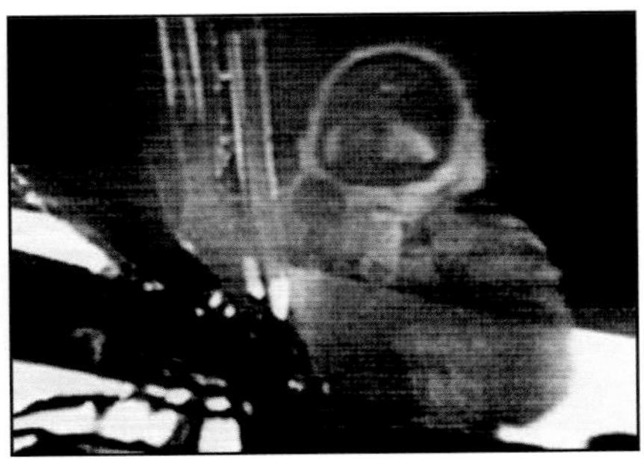

A television picture of astronaut Neil Armstrong about to take his 'giant leap for mankind'.

Other objectives included:

- the collection of lunar soil and rocks for analysis on return to Earth;
- the deployment of scientific experiments on the lunar surface; these included Laser Ranging Retro Reflectors (to monitor the Earth - Moon distance), passive seismometers, lunar dust collectors and solar wind composition (SWC) experiments.

At 02:56 GMT on July 21st 1969, Neil Armstrong was the first of a total of 12 astronauts to step onto the Moon's surface. Project *Apollo* continued after the series of successful manned landings (notably the *Skylab* and *Apollo-Soyuz* projects), but failed to attract as much public interest as the manned landings.

4.2 Origin of the Moon

There are many theories regarding how the Moon came into existence. The most popular theory is the **Giant Impact Hypothesis** in which a large body about the same size as Mars - astronomers call it Theia - struck a glancing blow with a nascent Earth. Theia was vaporised along with part of the Earth, and the debris slowly cooled and condensed to form the Moon.

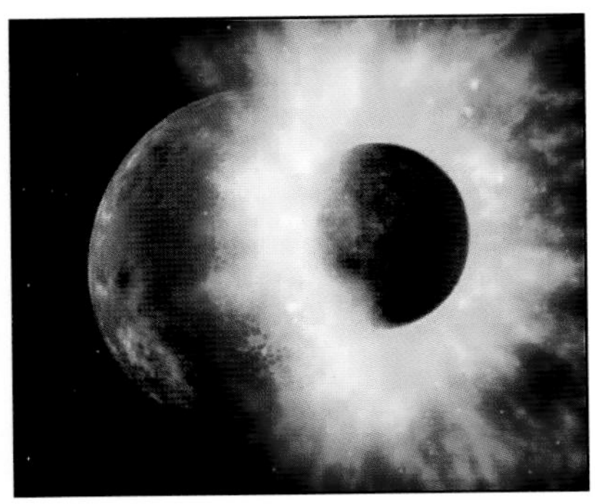

Artist's impression of the glancing blow between Theia and the Earth.

Alternative theories include:

- **Fission Theory**: The Earth was spinning so rapidly that part of it (now filled by the Pacific Ocean) spun off and formed the Moon;
- **Capture Theory**: The Earth and the Moon were formed at different places in the Solar System, but the Moon became 'captured' by Earth's gravitational force;
- **Condensation (Co-accretion) Theory**: The Earth and Moon formed together at the same time out of material from the solar nebula.

The Giant Impact Hypothesis is supported by the Moon's lack of substances that evaporate easily ('volatiles' such as water) and its small iron core; however, not all astronomers agree with this model and it remains a hypothesis.

A photograph by astronaut Michael Collins showing the Lunar Module *Eagle* descending to the lunar surface in July 1969.

That's Earth in the distance!

Image credit: NASA

Astronaut Buzz Aldrin deploys the SWC designed to collect solar wind particles.

Image credit: NASA

Splashdown of the *Apollo 11* Command Module off the coast of Hawaii before recovery to the aircraft carrier *USS Hornet*.

Image credit: NASA

STFC offers a loan scheme of meteorites and lunar rocks to schools and other educational institutions free of charge. Find out more at:

stfc.ac.uk

5.1 Planets and dwarf planets

5.2 Comets

5.3 Meteoroids and meteorites

5.4 The size of the Solar System

5.5 Optical telescopes

5.6 Space probes

Which planet in the Solar System:

1...could float on water?

2... has a rusty surface and is known as the *Red Planet*?

3...can appear brighter than any other planet in the sky?

Answers after Index

The dwarf planet Pluto with its largest moon Charon.

Image credit: NASA

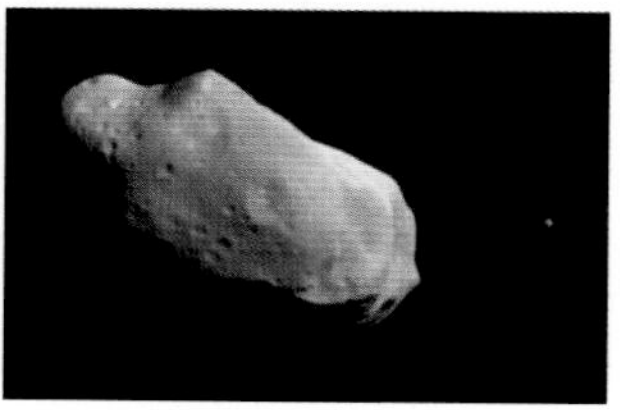

The asteroid Ida with its moon Dactyl in the distance.

Image credit: NASA/JPL

5 Exploring the Solar System

5.1 Planets and dwarf planets

The eight planets in our Solar System follow stable, almost circular, orbits around the Sun; they are all in the same sense and roughly in the same plane.

The planets can be split into two distinct groups. The four **terrestrial planets** are relatively small worlds of rock surrounding iron cores. In contrast, the four gaseous **giant planets** have liquid interiors and substantial atmospheres of hydrogen (H_2) and helium (He) with traces of methane (CH_4) and ammonia (NH_3); they are accompanied by complex ring systems and a large retinue of moons, some of which are larger than our Moon and even the planet Mercury.

The heavily-cratered, lunar-like planet Mercury. *Image credit: NASA*

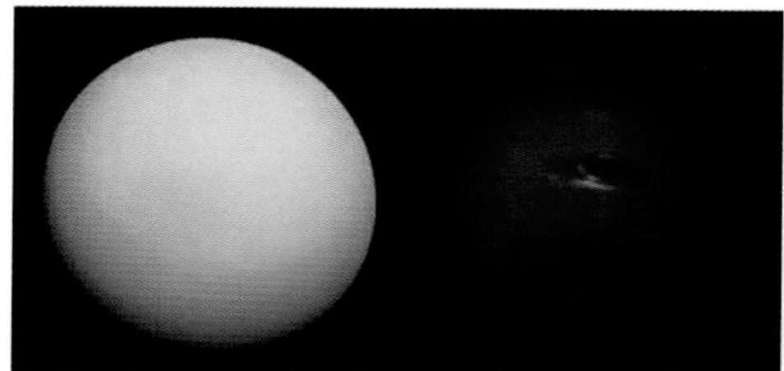

The 'twin' planets Uranus (left) and Neptune. *Image credit: NASA*

The table shows some of the principal characteristics of the planets.

planet	diameter /1000 km	mass / Earth mass	*T*/°C	atmosphere	rings?	moons
Mercury	4.9	0.055	170	tenuous	x	0
Venus	12.1	0.82	470	dense CO_2	x	0
Earth	12.8	1.00	15	N_2, O_2 & H_2O	x	1 (the Moon)
Mars	6.9	0.11	-50	thin CO_2	x	2
Jupiter	143	318	-150	H_2 & He	✓	>60
Saturn	121	95	-180	H_2 & He	✓	>60
Uranus	51	15	-210	H_2 & He	✓	>25
Neptune	50	17	-220	H_2 & He	✓	>12

Like true planets, **dwarf planets** have sufficient mass to be spherical, but lack the gravitational force needed to sweep their orbits clear of other debris.

With the exception of Ceres - this is the largest body in the main **Asteroid Belt** - most dwarf planets inhabit the cold outer limits of the Solar System: the **Kuiper Belt**. Notable dwarf planets include: Pluto, Eris and Makemake.

There is also a very large number of **Small Solar System Objects (SSSOs)** that include **asteroids** (small, irregular rocky objects with diameters < 1000 km), **meteoroids** (even smaller) and **comets** ('dirty snowball' mixtures of compacted dust, rock and ice, found mainly in the outer regions of the Solar System).

Most asteroids reside in the doughnut-shaped Main Belt between the orbits of Mars and Jupiter. Sizes range from ~ 10 m (the generally-accepted cut-off between asteroids and meteoroids) to ~ 1000 km; most have irregular shapes.

Comet Hale-Bopp was a rare visitor to the inner Solar System during the late 1990s.

Both the ion (blue) tail and the broader dust tail (yellow / white) are clearly visible.

Image credit: Bill Schwittek

5.2 Comets

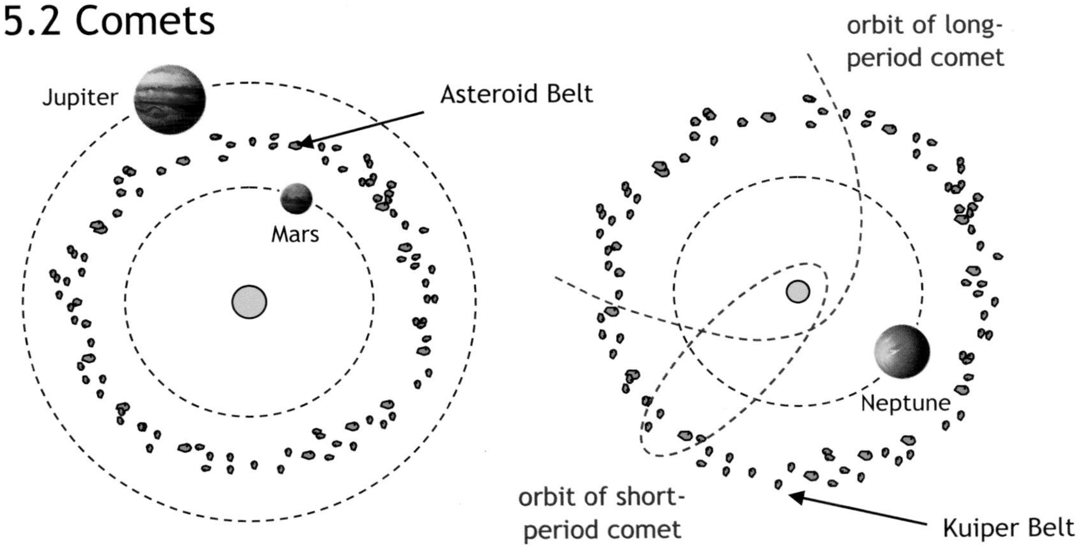

A teacher uses dry ice (solid CO_2), water, sand, soil, a splash of ammonia and a dash of Worcestershire Sauce to make a model comet, which his pupils are keen to photograph.

Image by the author

Comets can be classified in terms of their orbital periods:

- **Short-period** comets have periods < 200 y; most tend to hug the plane of the Solar System, and are thought to originate in the **Kuiper Belt** from where the gravitational influence of the planet Neptune might have 'nudged' some into elliptical solar orbits; a sub-set of these have periods < 20 y and do not venture much further away from the Sun than Jupiter;
- **Long-period** (> 200 y) comets originate in the **Oort Cloud**, a spherical distribution of icy bodies about half of the way to the nearest star; they have unpredictable orbits, with some highly-inclined to the plane of the Solar System and some orbiting in the opposite sense to that of the planets.

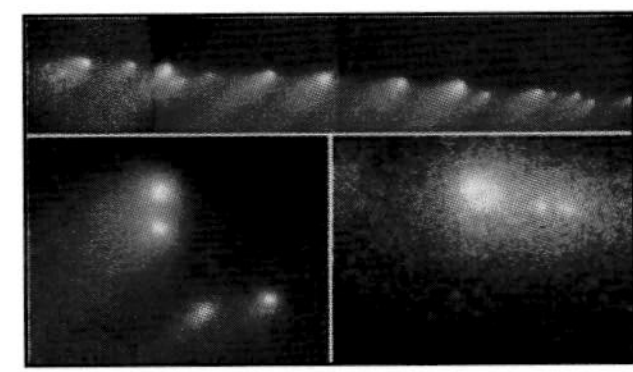

In 1994, Comet Shoemaker-Levy was captured by the gravitational field of Jupiter and torn apart. Fragments of the comet 'crashed' into the giant planet depositing dust and other debris into Jupiter's clouds.

Other comets can have their orbits 'modified' by the gravitational attraction of the massive planets.

Image credit: NASA

As a comet approaches the Sun, a **coma** of rarefied gasses and dust envelopes the small (~ 10 km) **nucleus** of rock and ice; eventually, one or more **tails** develop that can be several millions of kilometres long.

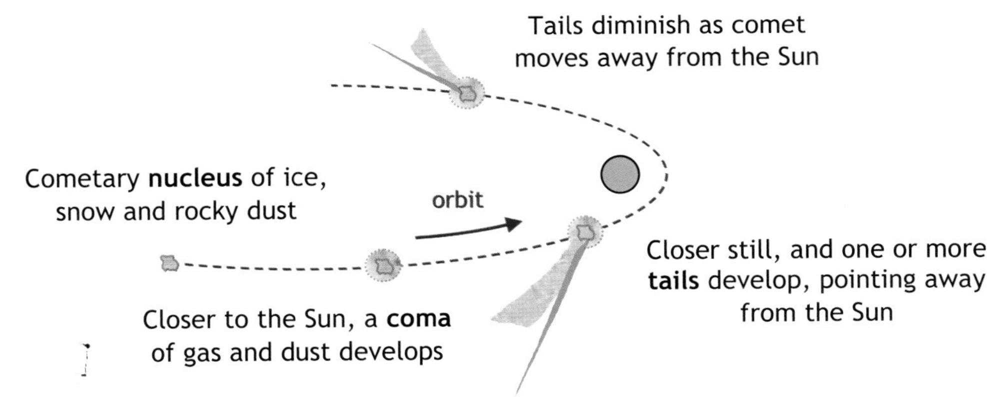

Keep up to date with cometary visitors and what else is happening in the night sky by signing up to *EarthSky News*.

For a free daily newsletter and links to other resources, visit:

earthsky.org

As the comet rounds and then begins to move away from the Sun, the tails and coma become less visible. Eventually the comet (now depleted of some of its content) ceases to be influenced by the solar radiation, fades from view and returns to the outer Solar System.

The ion and dust tails are clearly visible in this spectacular image of Comet West.

Image credit: John Laborde

It is the Sun that is primarily responsible for the formation of comets' tails, and so it should be no surprise that these generally point away from it.

A comet's **ion tail** is long, straight and predominantly blue in colour; it consists of charged atoms (ions) that have been excited by particles in the solar wind (see chapter 9) and emit light by fluorescence when they de-excite.

The broader, curved **dust tail** is produced by solar radiation pressure that pushes particles out of the comet's nucleus; these reflect sunlight, making the tail visible. The curvature is due to the individual grains of dust following their own independent solar orbits (having now been 'freed' from the comet).

For many years, scientists have argued about the origin of water on Earth.

Buttermere in the Lake District.

Water is an essential ingredient fo life, but what is its origin?

Was water produced by the outgassing of hydrogen and oxyge from primordial volcanoes, and/o was it deposited here by impacts with comets and/or giant asteroids

Image by the author

An artist's impression of the *Philae* lander on the surface of Comet 67P/Churyumov-Gerasimenko.

Image credit: ESA

Two of the main objectives of ESA's recent *Rosetta* mission were to study the activity of the icy surface of a comet (67P/Churyumov-Gerasimenko) as it approached the Sun, and to land a small probe (*Philae*) onto the comet's surface in order to perform a chemical analysis of its water content.

5.3 Meteoroids and meteorites

Meteoroids are particles of dust, larger grit-sized chunks of rocks, and boulder-sized mixtures of stone, ice and metal that are in orbit around the Sun.

Often, one such particle enters the Earth's atmosphere - speeds range from 20 - 70 km/s - where air resistance converts kinetic energy into thermal energy, heating smaller particles to incandescence. The resulting streak of light visible in the night sky is called a shooting star or **meteor**.

Meteorites are classified as either iron, stony or stony-iron types. Iron meteorites are rich in both iron and nickel; they probably originate from the metallic cores of asteroids that suffered huge impacts and broke apart.

Image credit: meteors-for-sale.com

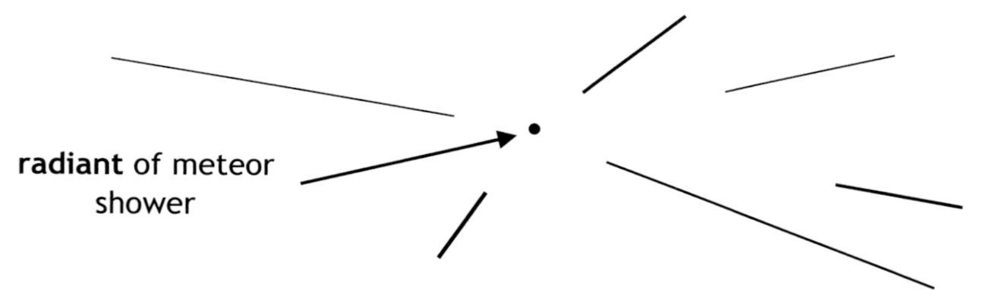

In a meteor shower, individual meteors appear to diverge from the radiant.

When the Earth passes through a dusty **meteoroid stream** in the wake of a comet, many more meteors are visible; the event is known as a **meteor shower**. The individual meteors appear to diverge from a 'vanishing point' called the **radiant**, which is simply due to perspective. The shower is named after the constellation in which the radiant lies.

A stony meteorite, most likely from the planet Mars.

Image credit: Natural History Museum

Larger meteoroids (probably from the Asteroid Belt, but possibly from the Moon or Mars) produce very bright meteors called **fireballs**; they survive their journey through the atmosphere, reaching the Earth's surface as **meteorites**.

Famous meteor showers include: The Perseids (every year in mid-August), Geminids (in November) and Quadrantids (in January).

It is interesting to note that the constellation of The Mural Quadrant (after which the Quadrantids shower is named) is now obsolete; the meteor shower was named ***before*** The Mural Quadrant failed to make the official list of 88.

Observational tasks A2 and B2 both involve observing a meteor shower and determining the radiant (point).

Task A2 uses the naked eye (easier) and B2 involves photographing the meteors (more accurate); a very wide-angle lens is needed for B2 since the meteors in a shower appear over a large area of sky.

With dark-adapted eyes, a red-filtered torch and a map of the appropriate part of the sky at the ready, task A2 involves sketching the meteor trails and then projecting these back (see dashed lines) to find the radiant.

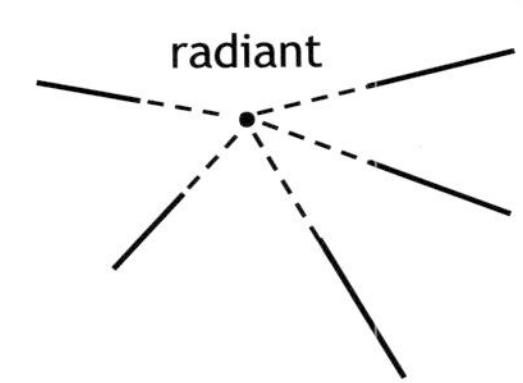

5.4 The size of the Solar System

Astronomers use specialist units when dealing with distances. The SI unit of length (the metre) is much too small: so are the kilometre and the mile.

Amateur astronomers and the media use the **light year** (*abbr*. l.y.) as their unit of distance; this is equivalent to the distance travelled by light in one year.

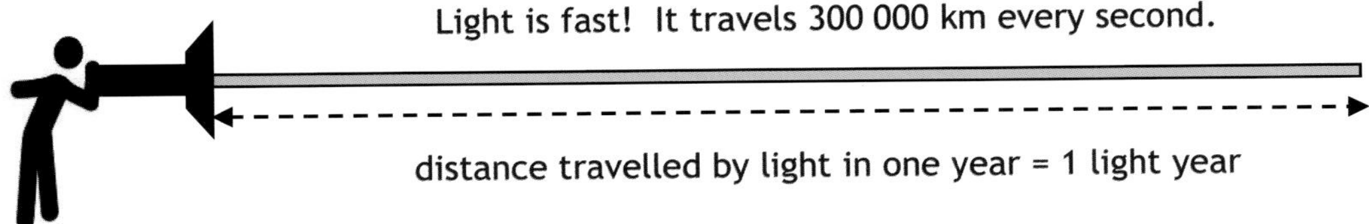

The nearest stars are a few light years away.

Professional astronomers use the **parsec** (*abbr*. pc) when dealing with distances to stars; we will define and explain this unit in chapter 13, but it is not very different from the light year (rather like the metre and the foot).

Distances within the Solar System are quoted in **astronomical units** (*abbr*. AU), where 1 AU is defined as a value equal to the mean distance from the Earth to the Sun:

$$1 \text{ AU} = 150 \text{ million km} = 1.5 \times 10^8 \text{ km}$$

There are plenty of questions (and answers) to develop and practise your mathematic skills converting distances in different units on our CD-ROM *Essential Maths Skills for GCSE (9-1) Astronomy*.

This is a convenient unit with which to compare the distances in the Solar System. For example, if somebody says that 'Saturn is 9.5 AU from the Sun', we know that the planet is 9.5 times further away from the Sun than we are.

The table lists some of the distances in our Solar System in astronomical units.

Mercury and Venus are called **inferior planets** because their orbits are closer to the Sun than that of the Earth.

Those further from the Sun are **superior planets**.

In comparison, the Moon is ~1/400 AU from the Earth.

object	distance from Sun / AU
Mercury	0.38
Venus	0.72
Earth	1.0
Asteroid Belt	~2 - 3
Saturn	9.5
Neptune	30
Kuiper Belt	~30 - 50
Oort Cloud	~5000 - 100 000

A portrait of Edmond Halley, the second Astronomer Royal, by Godfrey Kneller. Halley devised an ingenious method to determine the absolute size of the Solar System.

Image credit: Royal Museums Greenwich

300 years ago, astronomers knew the ***relative*** distances between the planets and the Sun: the ***scale*** of the Solar System. In 1677, English astronomer Edmond Halley (of Halley's Comet fame) formulated a plan to determine the ***absolute*** distance between two planets: the ***size*** of the Solar System.

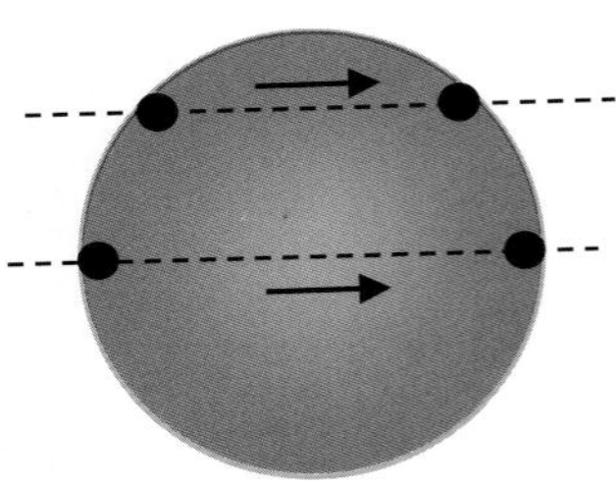

Observers at different latitudes on Earth observe different paths taken by the planet Venus (the black circle) across the Sun's disc.

Halley used geometry to show that the difference in path lengths would allow the absolute distance to Venus to be determined.

On rare occasions, one of the **inferior planets** (Mercury and Venus) crosses the solar disc; such an event is known as a **transit**. It was known that the observed paths (Halley called them **chords**) taken by Venus would vary from place to place because of parallax (just like the lunar libration from high latitudes).

Halley used geometry to show that the angle between two chords (α) could be calculated from the difference in their lengths; this in turn could be found by the difference between the times taken for Venus to cross the solar disc.

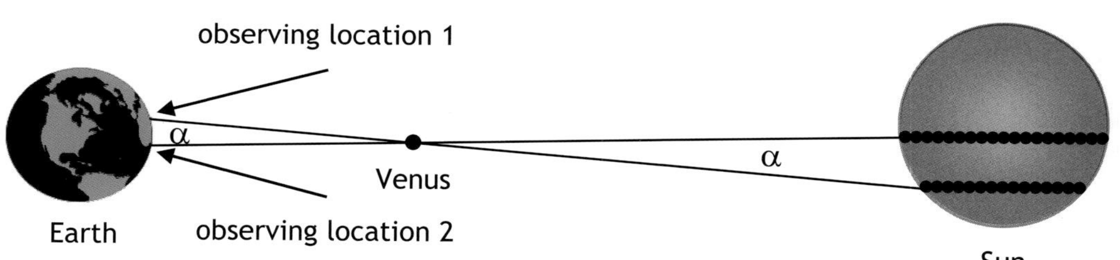

Halley showed that if the latitude distance between the two observing locations was known, simple triangulation could then be used to calculate the distance from Earth to Venus, and therefore from Earth to the Sun.

In 1716, Halley urged astronomers to travel to different latitudes to observe and time the forthcoming transits in 1761 and 1769. The request was taken up by the global scientific community, eventually allowing the astronomical unit to be determined to within 2.5% of its modern-day value.

Pupils photograph the transit of the planet Mercury that occurred in 2016. The Sun's disc is being projected onto paper for reasons of safety.

Transits come in close-pairs, but with very long timescales in between.

The next transits of Venus will be in 2117 and 2125.

Image by the author

5.5 Optical telescopes

There are two basic types of telescope: **refractors** and **reflectors**.

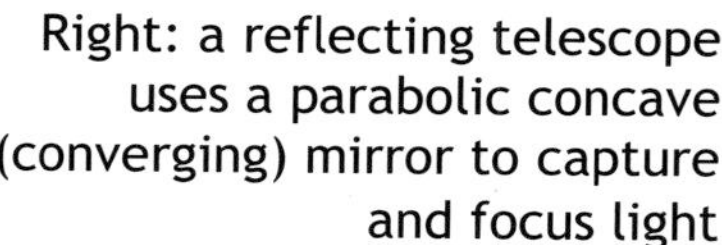

Left: a refracting telescope uses a convex (converging) lens to capture and focus light

Right: a reflecting telescope uses a parabolic concave (converging) mirror to capture and focus light

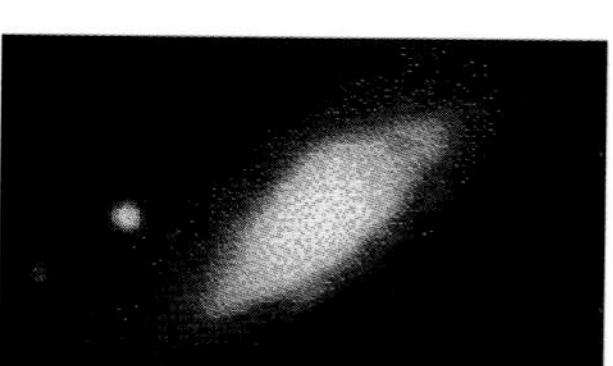

Two images of the Andromeda Galaxy. The top image shows poor/low resolution and very little detail can be seen: the galaxy might even be mistaken for the planet Saturn! The bottom image shows good/high resolution with much more detail.

The **objective element** collects as much light as possible and focuses the light to small bright image. This image is then magnified with an **eyepiece** lens so that astronomical objects such as double stars, lunar *maria*, globular clusters, nebulae and galaxies can be observed in much more detail (higher **resolution**) and are much brighter than when looking at them with just the naked eye.

A telescope's **size**, or **aperture,** is the diameter of its objective lens or mirror (usually quoted in cm, inches or metres). This should be of prime importance when using or purchasing a telescope because the larger the size:

- the more light enters the telescope, making images brighter;
- the 'sharper' the image, i.e. the higher the amount of detail that can be resolved.

The resolution also depends on the **wavelength** of light entering the telescope: the longer the wavelength the poorer the resolution, so in theory the amount of detail visible in images of pink/red nebulae is not as good as that seen in blue nebulae surround young stars.

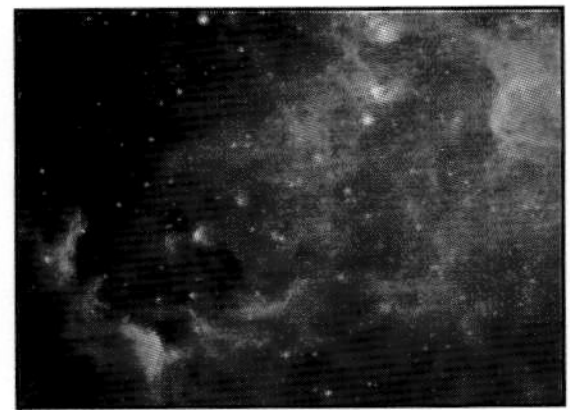
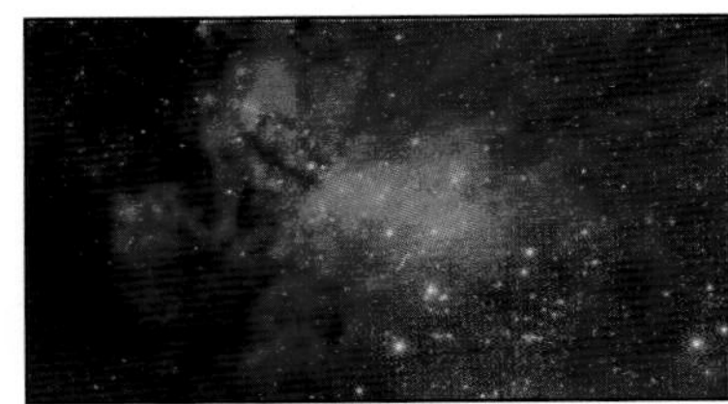
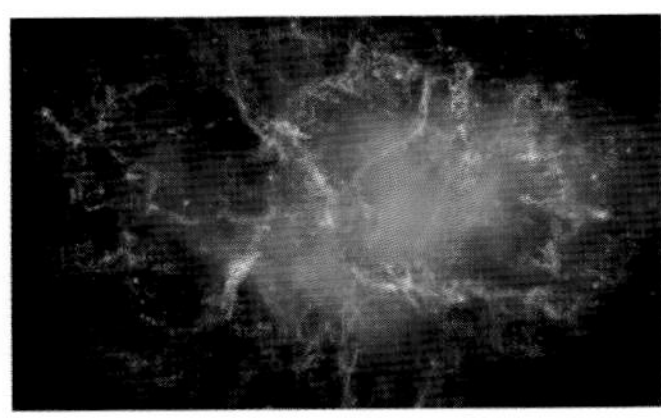

Through the same telescope, red images - red has the longest wavelength of visible light - are not as highly resolved as predominantly blue images. *Image credits: NASA*

A telescope's **light grasp** is a measure of how much light is captured by the objective element; this depends on its cross-sectional area. Being circular, area depends on the ***square*** of the diameter of the objective lens or mirror, so:

$$\text{light grasp} \;\alpha\; \text{area} \;\alpha\; (\text{diameter of objective element})^2$$

This means that if one telescope has an objective that has twice the diameter of another, its light grasp will be ***four*** times (2^2) greater.

Another important feature of a telescope is its **magnification**. This depends on the ratio of focal lengths of the objective (f_o) and eyepiece (f_e):

$$\text{magnification} = \frac{\text{focal length of objective}}{\text{focal length of eyepiece}} = \frac{f_o}{f_e}$$

(where the two focal lengths have the same unit: both in cm, both in mm etc.)

The focal length of the objective element is obviously fixed, and so different magnifications are achieved by using eyepieces of different focal lengths: the shorter the focal length, the greater the magnification.

A handy piece of kit for astronomers is a **Barlow lens** that isn't actually an eyepiece but allows eyepieces to be slotted into it. The optical elements of a Barlow lens increase the magnification by a factor of 2 or 3, effectively doubling the number of eyepieces available to the astronomer.

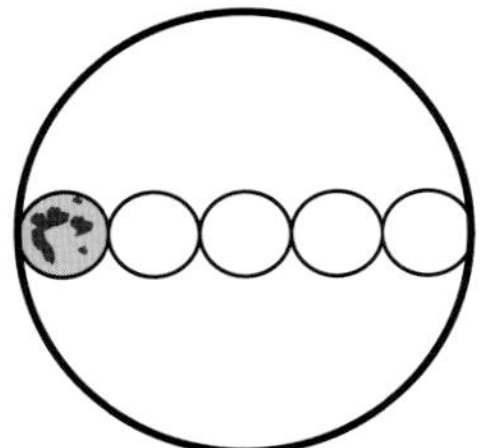

The ***greater*** the magnification, the ***smaller*** the field of view of the telescope

The field of view (FOV) of a telescope is the circle of sky that is visible through its eyepiece. For example, in the central image, the FOV is five Moon-widths, and the FOV in the right-hand image is slightly more than one Moon-width.

FOV is measured in degrees or minutes of arc (*abbr.* arcmin or ') where 1° = 60'. The full Moon subtends an angle of ~30' (0.5°) to an observer on Earth, and so the FOVs in the images above are ~150' and ~40' respectively.

The diameter of the objective lens of this refractor is 4 inches. A telescope's size (the diameter of the objective element) is much more important than its magnification when observing astronomical objects.

Desmond has a 6.0-cm refracting telescope and Molly has a 15-cm reflector.

How many times more is the light grasp of Molly's telescope compared with Desmond's?

Answer after Index

Telescope eyepieces can be interchanged to give different magnifications as desired.

Under poor seeing conditions, however, high magnification is undesirable since turbulence in the air gives rise to unsteady images that lack clarity.

There is a chapter dedicated to telescopes, including tutorials and a multitude of worked examples and practice questions on our CD-ROM *Essential Maths Skills for GCSE (9-1) Astronomy*.

Also, BBC Sky at Night magazine's excellent special edition *Back Garden Astronomy* gives many useful hints and tips on buying, using and getting the most out of telescopes.

The ISBN is: 977 23986680 0 1.

Italian astronomer and mathematician Galileo Galilei was the first scientist to use a telescope and interpret (sometimes incorrectly) what he saw.

Galileo's original telescope was a refractor with a convex lens as the objective and concave lens for an eyepiece.

The design was modified by German mathematician Johannes Kepler who replaced the concave eyepiece with a convex one.

There are many different types of telescope design, but most astronomers prefer to use reflectors, mainly because of the larger objective apertures that can be manufactured and supported (it is difficult for large lenses to keep their shape). Also, unlike lenses that absorb light, it is possible for mirrors to reflect light with almost no loss in intensity.

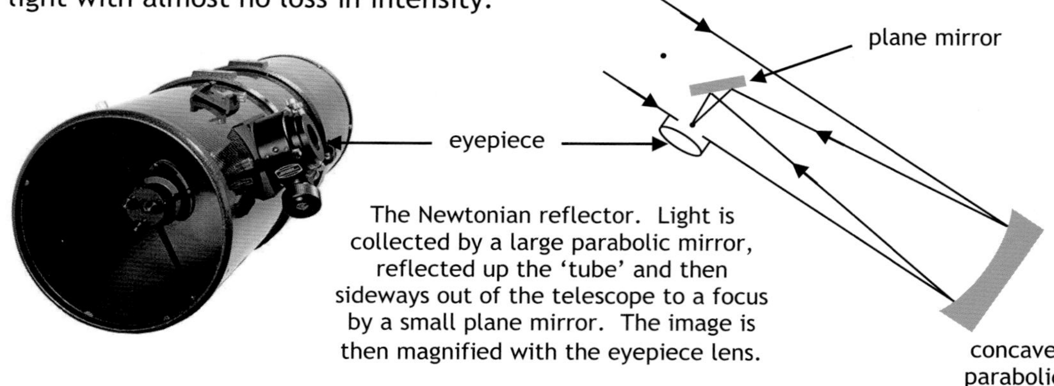

The Newtonian reflector. Light is collected by a large parabolic mirror, reflected up the 'tube' and then sideways out of the telescope to a focus by a small plane mirror. The image is then magnified with the eyepiece lens.

Another problem with refractors is that lenses tend to focus different wavelengths of light to slightly different points (this is known as **chromatic aberration**), making images blurred and unclear. Refractors also tend to be longer in size (although this can be avoided using prisms as in pairs of binoculars) which makes viewing difficult and impractical at times.

Detailed information on past, present and future European space missions can be found on the European Space Agency website:

www.esa.int

A diagram showing the optical arrangement of the Newtonian reflector is shown above. Another popular type of reflector is the Cassegrain reflector which tends to be more compact than the Newtonian.

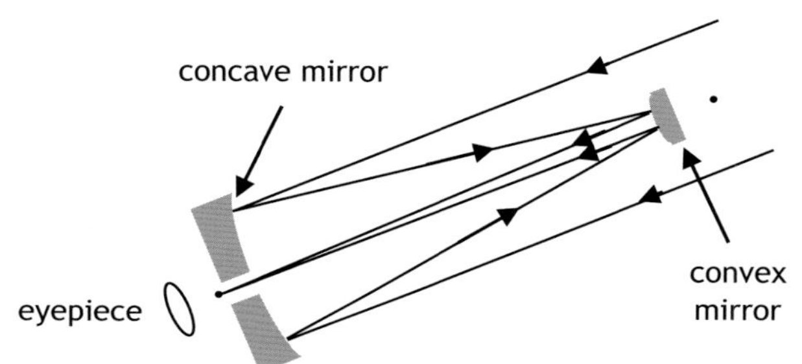

The Cassegrain reflector. Light is collected by a large parabolic mirror, reflected up and then back down the 'tube' by a small convex mirror. Light then passes through a small hole in the primary mirror where the image is magnified with the eyepiece lens.

5.6 Space probes

Exploring the Solar System using scientific instruments on unmanned space probes is one of the most exciting and challenging areas of Space Science. The four main types of probe, with examples from many years of exploration, are:

- **fly-by** missions, in which the space probe explores many targets; missions include *Voyagers I* and *II* (that visited the outer planets) and *New Horizons* (that explored Pluto and the outer Solar System);
- **orbiters**, such as the *Magellan* probe that mapped the planet Venus using radar, *Dawn* (that made detailed studies of asteroids Ceres and Vesta) and *Juno* (that measured Jupiter's composition and magnetosphere);
- **impactors**: we have already seen how the third stages of *Saturn V* rockets were impacted onto the lunar surface to cause artificial moonquakes; more recently, the *Deep Impact* probe impacted on Comet Temple 1 to study the internal composition of a comet;
- soft **landers**, in which the impact is controlled and the probe touches down intact on the surface; examples include *Huygens* landing on Saturn's moon Titan, the *Spirit* and *Opportunity* rovers to Mars and *Philae* (page 20).

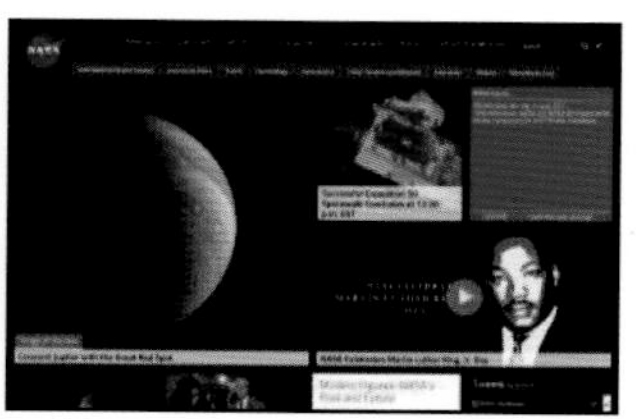

The latest information on US space missions can be found by exploring the NASA website:

www.nasa.gov

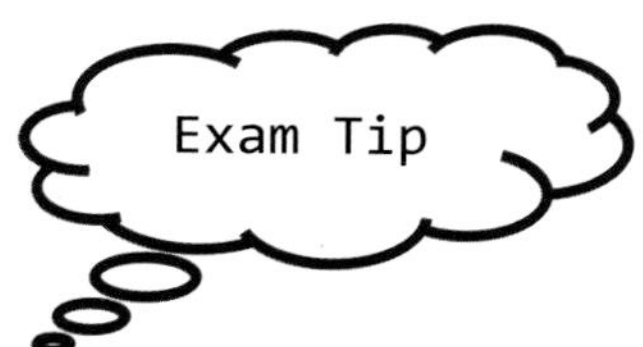

Students should be able to give some advantages and disadvantages of ***manned*** space exploration.

6 Solar System observation

6.1 Observing the planets

Since the dawn of civilisation, keen watchers of the night skies have noticed the changing positions of five points of light in relation to the other 'stars'.

The ancient Greeks called these 'wanderers' (Greek: *planetes*) from which the word 'planet' is derived. The Greeks noticed that the motion of planets was confined to a narrow **Zodiacal Band** that was centred on the Sun's motion and passed through 12 (or more) constellations. This can be explained by the fact that all the planets orbit the Sun in roughly the same plane.

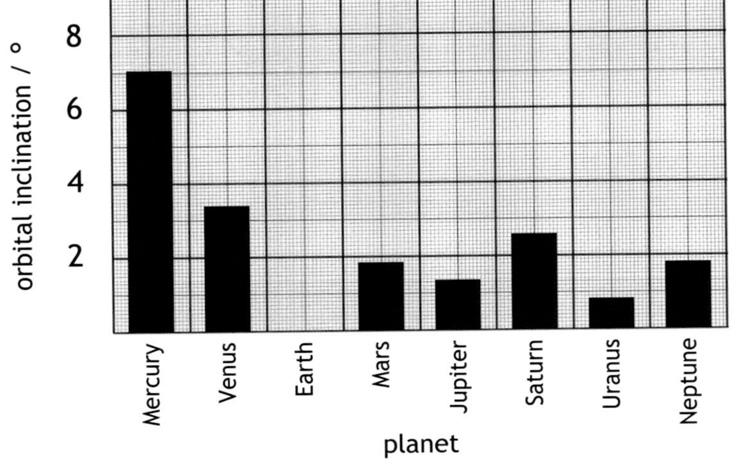

The bar chart shows the **orbital inclination** (i) for the planets; by definition, the inclination of the Earth's orbit is 0°.

The small values of i confine the planets to a narrow Zodiacal Band in the sky centred on the **ecliptic**.

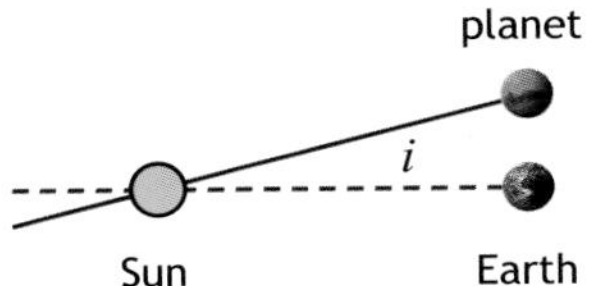

Orbital inclination is the angle between the plane of a planets' orbit and the plane of the Earth's orbit (the **ecliptic,** shown dashed) around the Sun.

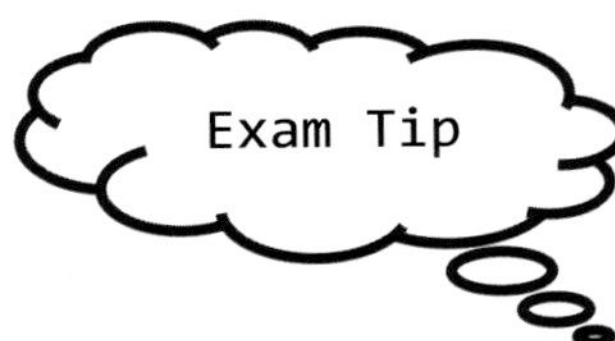

Ecliptic has two different meanings (see this page). Students should make sure that they can distinguish between them.

From night to night the planets move slowly eastwards, but ancient astronomers noticed that occasionally they appeared to travel backwards from east to west in either a 'loop-the-loop' or zigzag motion. This is known as **retrograde motion**.

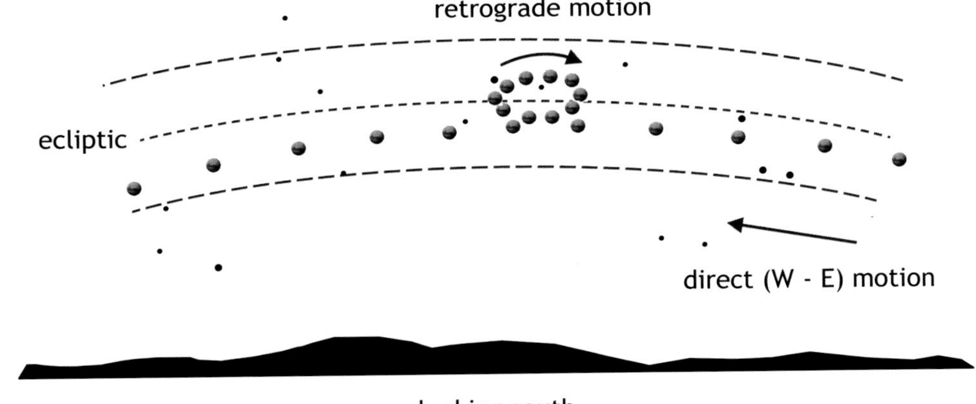

looking south

Ophiuchus, The Serpent Bearer, has recently been added to the official list of zodiacal constellations.

In the diagram, the position of a superior planet such as Mars is shown at weekly intervals. Retrograde motion can now be explained in terms of the faster-moving Earth 'overtaking' the superior planet on the inside of its orbit, but this caused huge problems for ancient astronomers (see next chapter).

The dashed lines indicate limits of the Zodiacal Band; these are ~8° either side of the ecliptic due to the relatively large orbital inclination of Mercury.

True or False?

(a) The nightly positions of the planets can be shown on a planisphere.

(b) Of the 8 planets in our Solar System, Venus's orbit is the most circular.

(c) When a planet undergoes retrograde motion, the planet physically moves backwards in its orbit for a few weeks.

Answers to all after Index

1. When a superior planet is at opposition, it is 4.2 AU from the Earth.

How far away is the planet when it is at conjunction?

2. When Venus is at inferior conjunction, it is 0.28 AU from the Earth.

Calculate the furthest possible distance between the Earth and Venus.

Answers to both after Index

This student is using the *Essential Maths Skills for GCSE (9-1) Astronomy* CD-ROM to help her to practise answering questions on planetary orbits like the ones in our Pop Quiz.

The planet Venus shines as the 'Morning Star' in the dawn sky shortly before sunrise. When this photograph was taken, Venus was close to greatest (western) elongation.

Image by the author

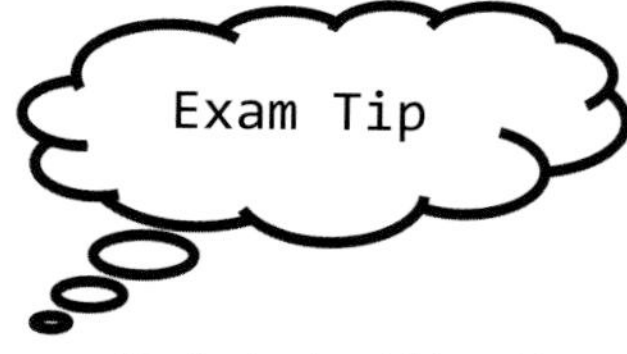

Students should be able to relate the ***position of the Sun*** on the celestial sphere at key dates in the year to its ***location above key latitudes*** on Earth.

For example, on June 21st (summer solstice) the Sun's celestial coordinates are 6 h, +23.5° and it lies directly above the Tropic of Cancer.

The optimum place in its orbit (marked with ✓) for a planet to be observed under the best (darkest sky) conditions depends on the planet's orbital position compared with that of the Earth (orbit shown as blue dashed lines).

We will consider key positions in the orbits of inferior and superior planets.

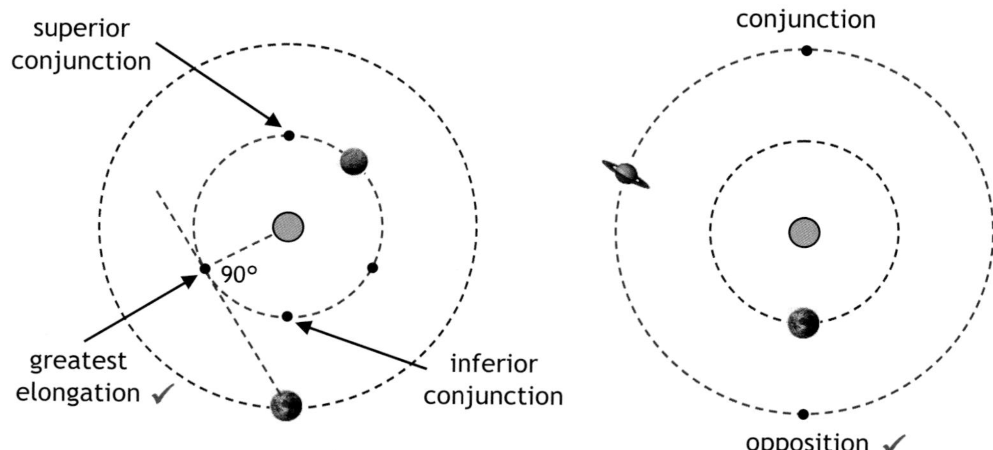

An inferior planet such as Mercury is best observed when it appears furthest from the Sun in the morning or evening sky; this is at, or close to, **greatest elongation** when the angle Sun - planet - Earth is 90°.

A superior planet is best observed at, or close to, **opposition**. At this point in its orbit, the planet is closest to Earth, at its brightest and opposite the Sun in the sky; it is possible to observe the planet all night long and with the highest resolution.

When it is at inferior conjunction, an inferior planet may undergo a **transit** of the Sun's disc. Transits, however, are extremely rare events due to the orbital inclinations taking the planet either 'above' or 'below' the Sun in the sky.

A more common event is an **occultation** in which a planet may temporarily obscure a distant star as it moves in front of the star for a few moments.

6.2 The apparent motion of the Sun

Let's leave the planets for now and look at the Sun's eastward journey across the celestial sphere during one year. Of course, the Sun isn't really moving: its apparent motion is due entirely to the orbital motion of the Earth and the constant 23.5° tilt of the Earth's equator to the ecliptic.

The position of the Sun on March 21st marks the zero of right ascension (page 9) at the **First Point of Aries** (denoted ♈). The graph below shows the celestial coordinates of the Sun over the course of a year. ♎ denotes the **First Point of Libra**, where the Sun returns to the southern hemisphere on September 23rd.

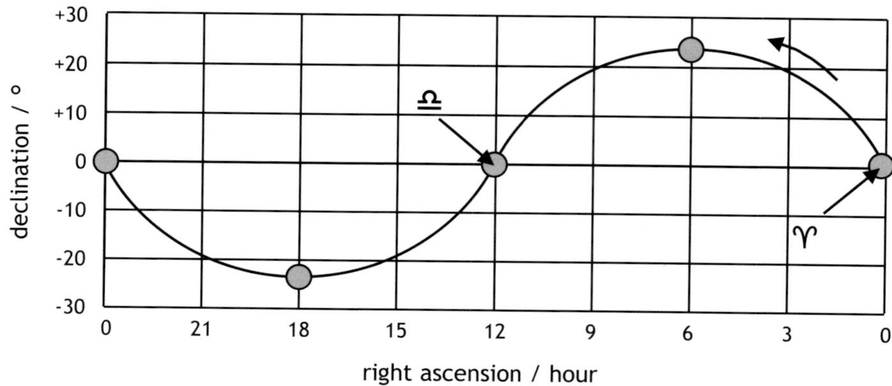

7 Early models of the Solar System

7.1 Solar and lunar cycles

Ancient civilisations were well aware of the various regularities in the positions of the planets, stars, the Sun and the Moon on a range of different timescales. For example, detailed observations showed that the Moon repeated its cycle of phases every 29.5 days and that the seasons were related to the length of the day and the height of the Sun in the sky.

The flooding of the River Nile (above) was very important to ancient Egyptians because water, mud and silt were washed up onto the banks making fertile growing areas. As soon as the floods receded, the Egyptians ploughed the soil, sowed their seeds and used animals to push them into the ground. The Egyptians used the time at which the bright star Sirius rose after sunset to predict when the Nile would flood.

Astronomy was therefore born out of the basic need for human survival: when to sow and harvest crops, pick fruits and nuts, and hunt for antelope and buffalo. The 'celestial calendars' were key to the ancients' very existence.

As ancient civilisations flourished, stone monuments and temples were built to act as ceremonial and/or religious observatories. Many were aligned to the positions of key stars (for example the three stars in Orion's Belt) or to the rising of the Sun on key dates of the year (for example the summer solstice).

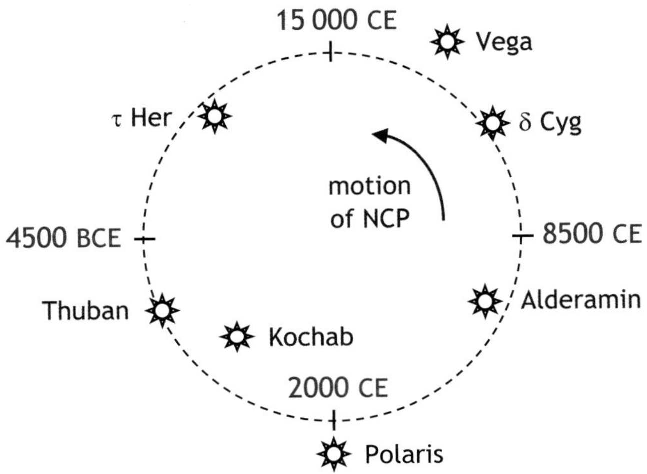

As the Earth's axis precesses, different stars can be found at the North Celestial Pole

However, the current celestial alignments of many ancient monuments differ from their original alignments because the Earth's axis of rotation is not fixed but traces out a circular path against the stars.

This relatively slow gyroscopic 'wobbling' of the Earth's axis is called **precession**, and it arises from the gravitational pull of the Moon and the Sun on the Earth's equatorial bulge; one complete rotation of the Earth's axis takes ~26 000 y.

Stonehenge is one of the most famous and important stone circles in Britain. It was built in stages between *c.*3000 BCE and *c.*1500 BCE and its purposes remain a mystery: an astronomical observatory, a place of healing, and a site for funerals and religious ceremonies have all been suggested.

An evocative photograph of Stonehenge at sunset.

Image credit: Jia Shen

An ancient Egyptian calendar based on a year of 365 days in one year and 30 days in one month.

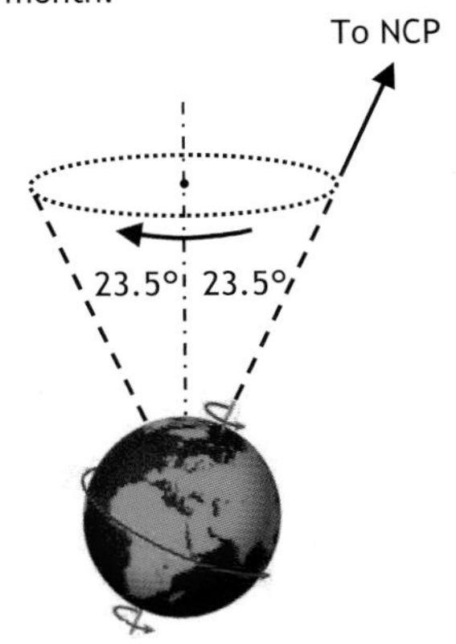

Five 'wandering' planets were known to the ancient Greeks.

Can you name them all?

Answer after Index

7.2 Models of the Solar System

Early models of the 'Universe' were based on the **geocentric** (Earth-centred) systems of ancient Greek philosophers such Plato and Aristotle.

The Aristotelian Universe was based on four 'elements' - earth, air, fire and water - and a system of concentric crystalline spheres driven by a 'prime mover' that carried the Moon, Sun, planets and fixed stars around the Earth.

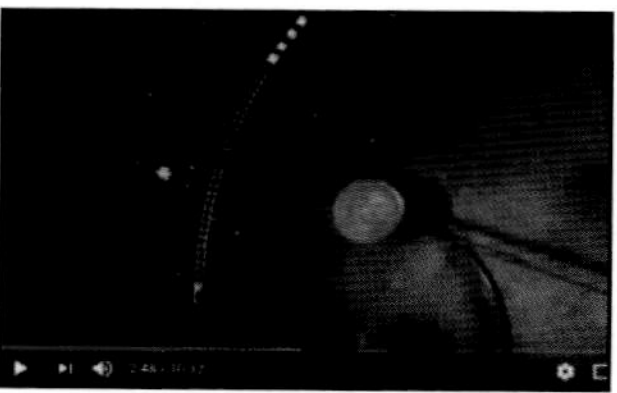

A short YouTube clip presented by US astronomer Carl Sagan includes mechanical models showing Ptolemy's epicycles and how they could explain the motion of the known planets:

www.youtube.com/watch?v=faqjmAoXpM4

A 17th century print of the Aristotelian Universe: in the Sublunar Sphere, the 4 elements were changeable, temporary and 'corruptible', but in the Superlunar Sphere (Heavens), everything was changeless, pure and 'perfect'.

One of the major problems with this model was the inability to explain the observed retrograde motion of the planets (see page 25). In a modification (left), each planet was placed on a small rotating circle (an **epicycle**) whose centre revolved around the Earth on another circle (the **deferent**).

An (unknown) artist's impression of the Egyptian astronomer Claudius Ptolemaeus (Ptolemy), whose 'model' of the Universe lasted for ~1500 years

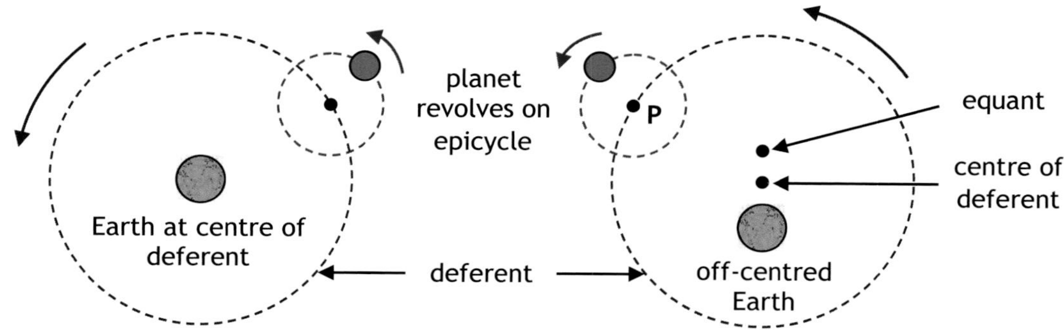

In the Greek model, the planets revolved on epicycles whose centres revolved around the Earth.

Ptolemy made subtle modifications to the Greek model that closely matched the observed motion of the planets.

These refinements were still unable to explain the exact positions and changing speeds (and directions) of the planets, and required further modification by the Egyptian astronomer and geographer Claudius Ptolemaeus (Ptolemy).

> *'If the Lord Almighty had consulted me before embarking upon his creation, I should have recommended something simpler.'* **Alfonso X of Castile, Spanish monarch and astronomer**

Danish Sculptor Bertel Thorvaldsen's fine statue of Nicholas Copernicus in the centre of Warsaw, Poland

Image by the author

Ptolemy retained the epicycles but making two additional small adjustments (above right) that involved a slightly off-centred Earth and an imaginary point called the **equant** from which the angular motion of the centre of each epicycle (**P**) was uniform. A little complicated you might think!

Ptolemy's model, however, gained general acceptance for almost 1500 years until the Polish monk Nicholas Copernicus applied some mathematical modelling to the problem and advocated a **heliocentric** (Sun-centred) Universe.

Copernicus was not the first to propose such a model - Aristarchus of Samos (of whom we will learn more later) argued for a heliocentric Universe *c.*270 BCE based on his calculations that the Sun was much larger than the Earth - but unlike previous schemes, a model with the Sun at its centre could explain the observed motion of the planets without the need for an equant and epicycles.

NICOLAI
COPERNICI TO

The cover and an extract from Copernicus' book *De revolutionibus orbium coelestium*, published in 1543

Copernicus was reluctant to present his model to the world - some say that he did not wish to place himself in conflict with the Church, and others say that it was for fear of being ridiculed and 'hissed off the stage' by his peers - but in 1543, as he lay dying, Copernicus finally published his book *De revolutionibus orbium coelestium* (On the Revolutions of the Heavenly Spheres).

The heliocentric model was gaining acceptance in the late 16th century, but astronomers were keen to reduce the disagreement between the predicated (by mathematics) positions and true (observed) positions of the planets.

Left: A portrait of Danish astronomer Tycho Brahe by the artist Tobias Gemperlin. **Middle**: A drawing of Uraniborg, Tycho's castle in which he housed his many observational instruments. Right: A portrait of Johannes Kepler (artist unknown) who became Tycho's assistant in Prague in 1600.

An engraving of Tycho's large mural quadrant with which it was possible to determine the positions of stars and planets accurately and to a high degree of precision (some say the nearest sixtieth of a degree, or 1 arcmin)

The most prominent astronomer of this era was the eccentric Tycho Brahe who, under the patronage of Frederick II, the King of Denmark, built the Uraniborg Observatory on the island of Hven that lay between Denmark and Sweden.

Tycho was particularly interested in the motion of the planet Mars and plotted its position systematically and with great precision for over 20 years. In 1600, Tycho was joined by a German mathematician called Johannes Kepler who became his assistant.

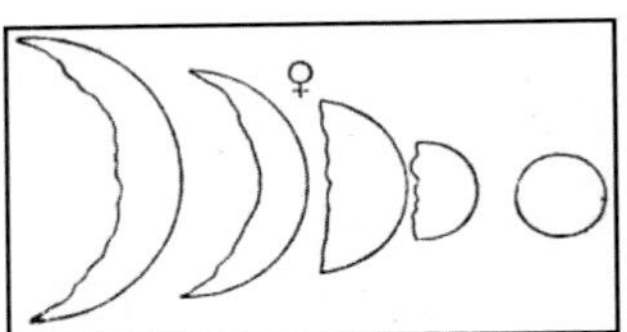

Galileo's sketches of the planet Venus. The changing size of Venus showed that it could not be orbiting a central Earth.

Image credit: Istituto di Linguistica Computazionale

In 1601, Tycho died suddenly. Some sources tell us that it was due to a bladder infection acquired through excessive drinking, but others suggest that Tycho died through mercury poisoning. Kepler was now free to analyse Tycho's positional data for Mars and formulated his three laws of planetary motion (page 30) which he published in *Astronomia nova...* (The New Astronomy) in 1609, and *Harmonices mundi* (The Harmony of the World) in 1619.

In this fresco by Giuseppe Bertini, Galileo is seen demonstrating his newly-acquired 'optick tube' to the Doge of Venice.

1609 was also the year in which Italian mathematician and astronomer Galileo Galilei used his 'optick tube' (telescope) to observe the skies and make sketches of what he saw. Two of Galileo's observations in particular gave firm support to the heliocentric Universe and helped to establish its acceptance:

- The apparent size of the planet Venus changed and showed phases;
- Four moons (Galileo called them 'satellites') orbited the planet Jupiter.

Galileo's sketches of the planet Jupiter and its four 'Galilean' moons. These observations proved that the Earth was not the centre of all heavenly motion.

8 Planetary motion and gravity

8.1 Orbits and Kepler's first and second laws

Kepler's first law of planetary motion states that the planets move in elliptical orbits around the Sun, with the Sun at one focus (*pl.* foci) of each ellipse (the other focus is empty).

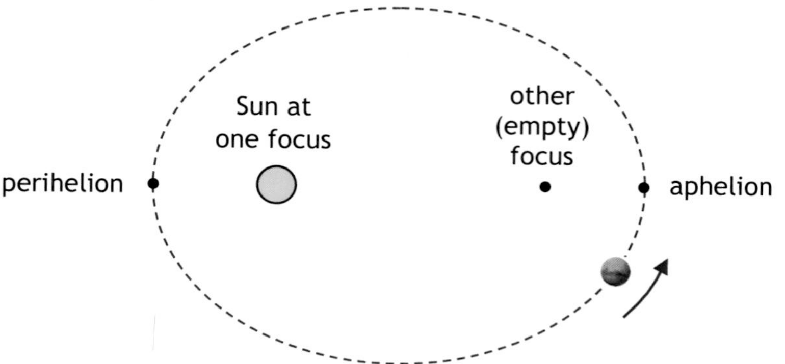

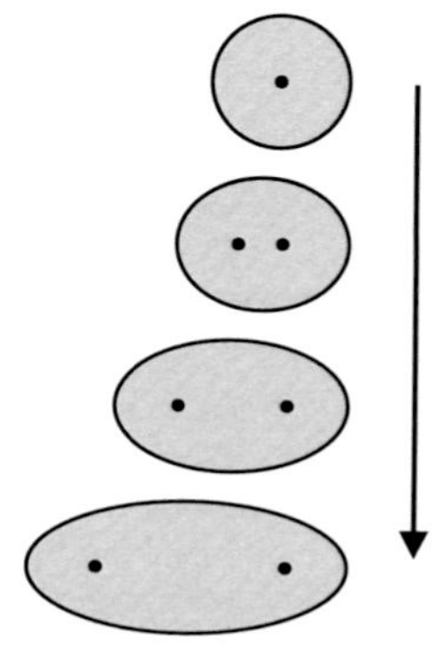

The diagram above shows a number of ellipses of increasing **eccentricity** (the first is a circle, for which the two foci coincide).

The points in the orbit at which a planet is closest to and furthest from the Sun are called **perihelion** and **aphelion** respectively. In reality, the difference between them is nowhere near as great as depicted in the diagram. In fact, the orbit of Venus is almost a perfect circle.

Kepler's second law stares that an imaginary line from the Sun to a planet sweeps out equal areas in equal intervals of time.

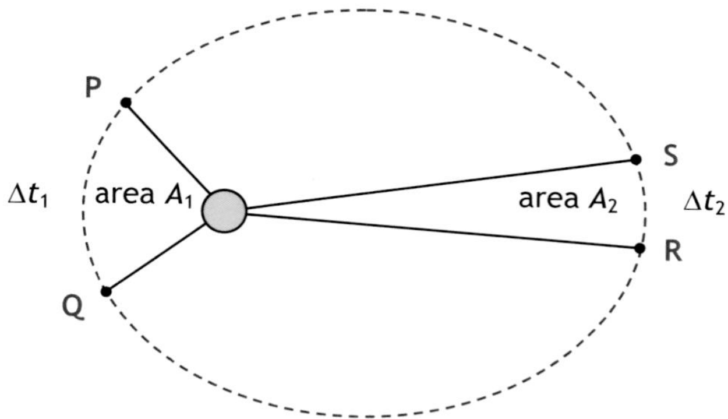

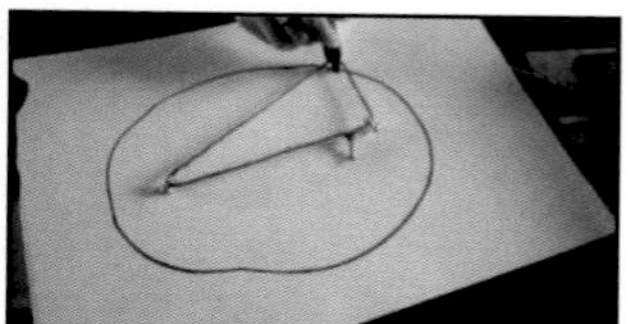

An ellipse can be drawn with the aid of two thumb pins (at the foci), a taught loop of string, a pencil and a sheet of card: the closer together the thumb pins, the less 'squashed' or eccentric (oval-shaped) the ellipse.

In the diagram, 'swept out' areas A_1 and A_2 are equal. The law states that the time taken for a planet to travel from **P** to **Q** occurs in the same time interval as when it is travelling from **R** to **S**, i.e. $\Delta t_1 = \Delta t_2$. Since distance **PQ** is greater than **RS**, this mean that a planet will be travelling fastest when close to perihelion and slowest when close to aphelion.

For a body orbiting the Earth, such as the International Space Station (ISS) pictured above, the closest and furthest points in the orbit are called **perigee** and **apogee** (see also page 15).

Image credit: NASA

Once again, the difference in speeds for planets is much less than the difference for bodies that have much more eccentric orbits such as comets.

It is interesting to note that the Earth is at perihelion, and travelling at its highest speed around the Sun, in early January (4th - 6th in most years). In theory then, our northern winters should be shorter and our summers longer!

8.2 Kepler's third law

Kepler's third law states that the square of the orbital period (T) of a planet is proportional to the cube of its mean distance (r) from the Sun.

This can be written mathematically as:

$$T^2 \propto r^3 \quad \text{or} \quad \frac{T^2}{r^3} = \text{a constant}$$

The table shows data for some of the planets in the Solar System. The last column clearly shows that Kepler's third law is true for this particular system of orbiting bodies.

planet	r / AU	T / y	r^3 / AU^3	T^2 / y^2	T^2 / r^3 / arbitrary units
Venus	0.72	0.62	0.373	0.384	1.0
Earth	1.00	1.00	1.00	1.00	1.0
Jupiter	5.2	11.9	141	142	1.0
Saturn	9.5	29.5	857	870	1.0
Neptune	30	165	27 000	27 200	1.0

However, Kepler's laws can be shown to be true for ***any*** system of orbiting bodies such as artificial satellites around the Earth or the moons of Jupiter.

The only thing that will change in different orbiting systems will be the 'constant' in the equation above (let's call it k). It can be shown that k depends inversely on the mass (M) of the central body (the Sun, the Earth, Jupiter).

This can also be written mathematically as:

$$\frac{k_1}{k_2} = \frac{M_2}{M_1}$$

In the table above, the value of k is 1.0 unit; let this be k_1 and the Sun's mass be M_1. If we could obtain data for a system of planets around another star - ***these would have to be in the same units of AU and years*** - we could deduce the value of k_2; let's say it was 3.0 units.

This would mean that the value of k for this second star system was 3 times greater the value of k for ours. This would imply that the mass of its central star is 3 times ***smaller*** (that's the inverse bit) than that of the Sun.

The reason why the time periods and mean orbit radii are related to the mass of the central body is that the force responsible for the orbital motion of satellites and planets is that of **gravitation (gravity)**. This is an attractive force between ***all*** bodies that have mass.

8.3 Gravitation

In the summer of 1666, a young Isaac Newton was sitting under an apple tree in his garden at Woolsthorpe Manor in Lincolnshire, contemplating the motion of the Moon. Suddenly and without warning, an apple fell from the tree and hit Newton on the head. 'That's it,' cried Newton, 'I have discovered gravity.'

There are tutorials and plenty of worked examples and practice questions involving Kepler's laws (and his third law in particular) in the *Essential Maths Skills for GCSE (9-1) Astronomy* CD-ROM available now from Mickledore Publishing.

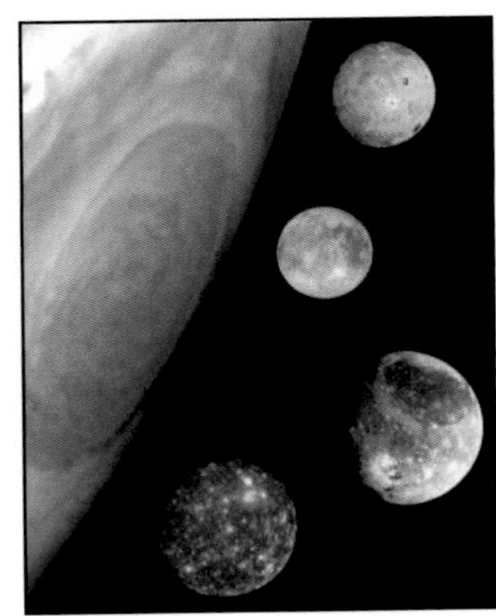

Kepler's laws hold true for ***any*** system of orbiting bodies such as the moons of Jupiter, the largest of which are shown here in this composite image.

Image credit: NASA

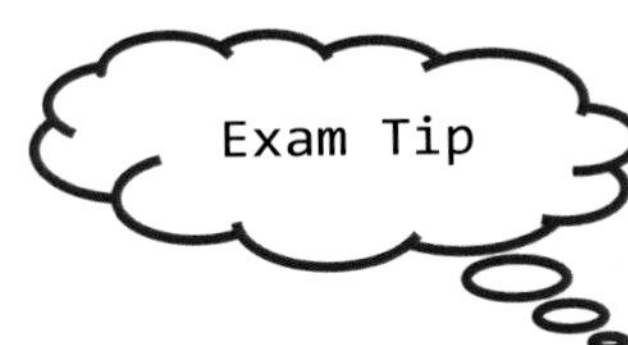

In questions involving calculations, it is important that students ***show all the working out*** to arrive at their final answer.

Students should also make sure that the **unit** is given and that the final answer contains an ***appropriate number of significant figures*** (no more than those given in the question).

In addition to making planets and satellites move in their orbits, gravitation is also responsible for lots of fun things!

This apple tree outside Trinity College in Cambridge is claimed to be a direct descendent from the tree in the gardens of Woolsthorpe Manor that is said to have inspired Newton to devise his theory of universal gravitation.

A portrait of Isaac Newton (*c.*1690) aged 46 by artist Godfrey Kneller.

Newton published the first of three editions of his work on gravitation in 1687. His book is commonly known by its shortened Latin title *Principia* (Mathematical Principles of Natural Philosophy).

When an asteroid is at aphelion (**A**), it is 8 times further from the Sun than when it is at perihelion (**P**).

Deduce the ratio:

$$\frac{\text{force on asteroid at } \mathbf{P}}{\text{force on asteroid at } \mathbf{A}}$$

Answer after Index

There's a nice YouTube clip showing Newton's cannon at:

https://www.youtube.com/watch?v=MpiknSRTmT4

Or so the story goes!

What we do know is that Newton somehow made a connection between falling apples and the orbit of the Moon around the Earth: both moved in the way that they did because of the universal force of gravitation.

Newton's law of universal gravitation states that every body in the Universe attracts every other body with a force that is directly proportional to the product of their masses and inversely proportional to the square of their distance apart (separation).

Hence gravitation is responsible for creating stable elliptical (or circular) orbits of moons around planets and planets around stars, maintaining the motion of stars around the centre of our Galaxy, causing the Andromeda Galaxy to be on a direct collision course with ours, and slowing down the rate at which the Universe is expanding. Impressive stuff!

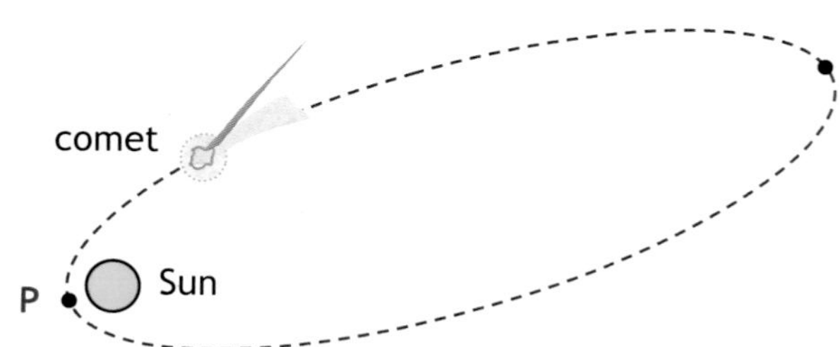

comet is 20x further from the Sun at aphelion compared with when at perihelion

The ***inverse square*** nature of the law is interesting: suppose that a comet orbits the Sun in such an eccentric orbit that when it is at aphelion (**A**), it is 20 times further from the Sun than when it is at perihelion (**P**).

This means that when the comet is passing through perihelion, the force of gravity acting on it from the Sun is 400 times (that's 20 ***squared***) greater than when it is at aphelion.

In order to explain orbits, Newton devised a 'thought experiment' in which a cannon, strategically placed on the summit of a high mountain, fired cannonballs at different horizontal velocities, A (the slowest) to E (the fastest).

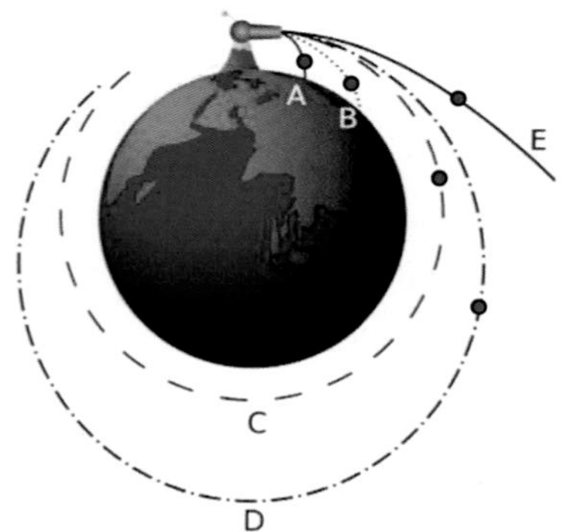

'Newton's cannon' fires cannonballs at different horizontal velocities from a high mountain.

The velocities of cannonballs A and B are too slow to go into an orbit around the Earth.

Then velocities of cannonballs D and E are too high for a circular orbit, but cannonball C has the exact velocity to go into a circular orbit.

Newton was able to show mathematically that the cannonballs would follow different orbits whose shapes (circle, ellipse, parabola etc.) depended on the initial horizontal velocities of each cannonball.

Orbit C corresponds to a circular orbit: the cannonball's horizontal velocity is 'just right' (slightly under 8 km/s) to cause the cannonball to 'fall' towards the Earth but by exactly the same amount that the Earth is curving away from it.

9 Solar astronomy

9.1 Observing the Sun

WARNING

Do not look directly at the Sun with the naked eye or any unfiltered optical instruments

Although the Sun can be observed safely using pinhole projection (see right), the best methods to obtain a large image of the Sun can be obtained by using:

- an H-alpha filter: this absorbs all sunlight apart from a very narrow range of wavelengths centred on a particular spectral line of hydrogen (λ = 656 nm);
- telescopic projection: this requires the use of a 'baffle' (card with a small hole) to absorb most of the solar radiation before entering the telescope.

Pinhole projection can be used to observe the Sun, but the projection card needs to be a long way from the pinhole to obtain a decent-sized image.

This NASA/JPL website shows you how:

http://www.jpl.nasa.gov/edu/learn/project/how-to-make-a-pinhole-camera/

Left: A teacher observes sunspots safely through a telescope fitted with an H-alpha filter. Right: Pupils observe a transit of Mercury using the telescope projection method; note the 'baffle' to prevent excessive radiation entering the telescope. *Images by the author*

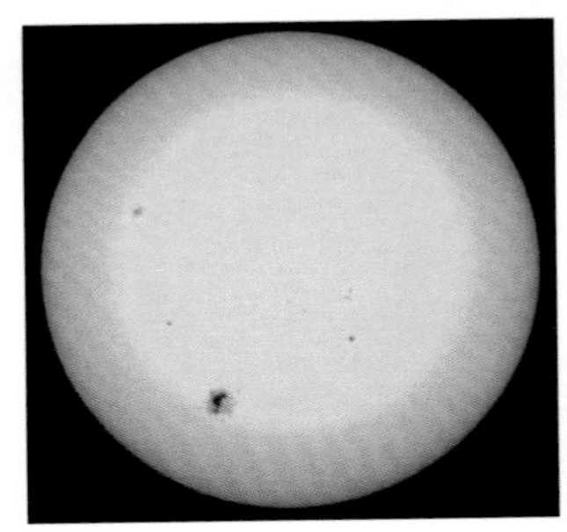

Several sunspots can be seen on the Sun's photosphere.

Image credit: NASA/JPL

On most clear days, observers can see a number of **sunspots** on the 'surface' (**photosphere**) of the Sun. These are cooler areas of the photosphere that correspond to strong localised magnetic fields that inhibit the upward motion of convective solar material and prevent it from reaching the photosphere.

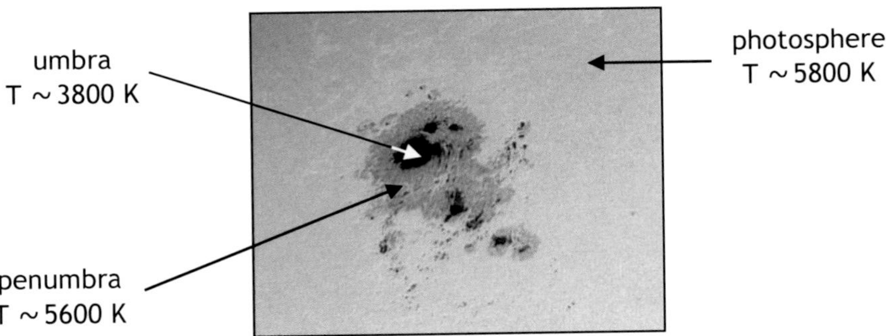

By observing the apparent motion of sunspots across the solar disc, it is possible to determine the Sun's rotation period at different latitudes and deduce that the Sun does not rotate as a solid body: its rotation period varies from 25 days at the solar equator to 36 days close to its poles.

Observational tasks A6 and B6 involve using drawings or photographs of sunspots to determine the rotation period of the Sun at a particular latitude.

Full details can be found in the *New Pupil Toolkit for GCSE (9-1) Astronomy*.

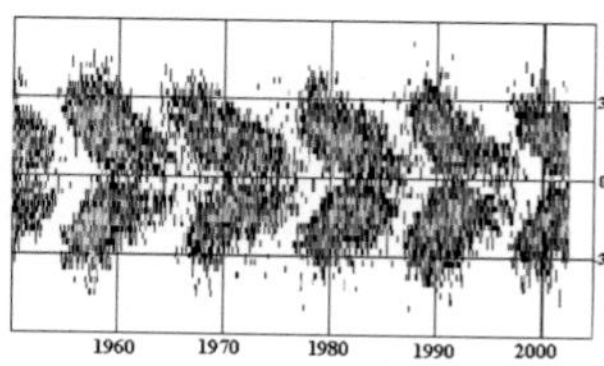

Individual sunspots are relatively short-lived - most last for a few days to a month - but the numbers and latitudes of sunspots follow a regular **solar cycle** of 11 years.

The relative numbers and latitudes can be shown on a **Butterfly Diagram**, so-called because of its resemblance to butterfly wings.

The cycle begins with relatively few spots at mid latitudes. During the next 11 years, the number appearing rises and falls, and there is a steady drift in latitude towards the solar equator.

1. At a particular latitude, the rotation period of the Sun is 30 days.

How many days will it take the Sun to rotate by 120°

2. At a different latitude, the Sun rotates through 60° in 5.5 days.

Calculate the Sun's rotation period for this latitude.

Answers to both after Index

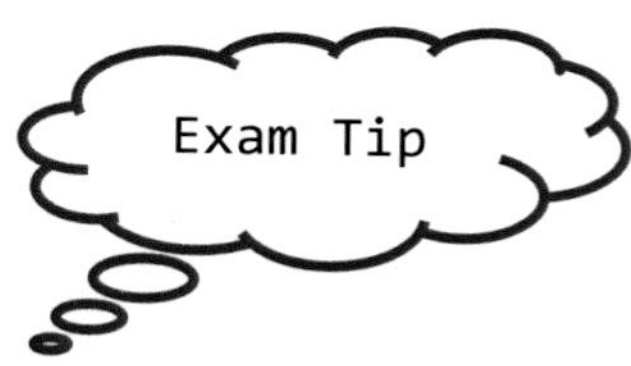

In questions asking students to describe the Sun's energy source, it is important to refer to ***nuclei*** of hydrogen and helium and **NOT *atoms***.

The solar rotation period can be determined from recording the position of a sunspot (or group) at approximately the same time every few days.

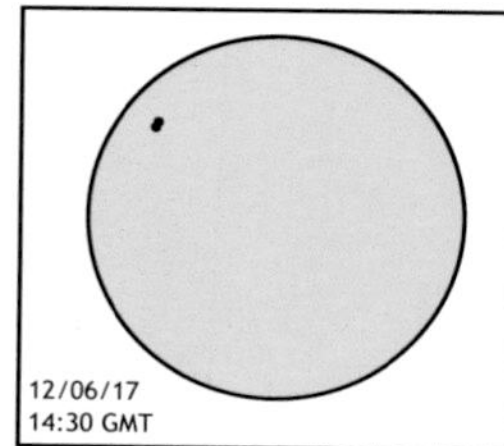

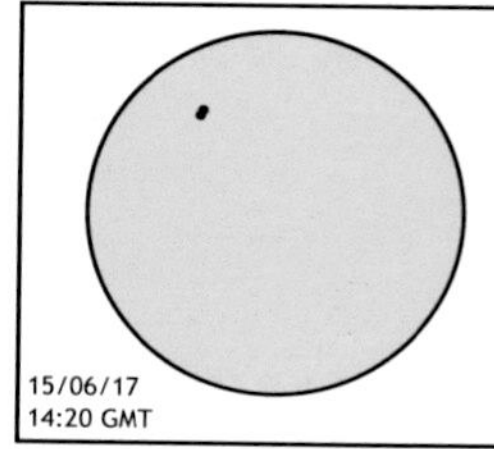

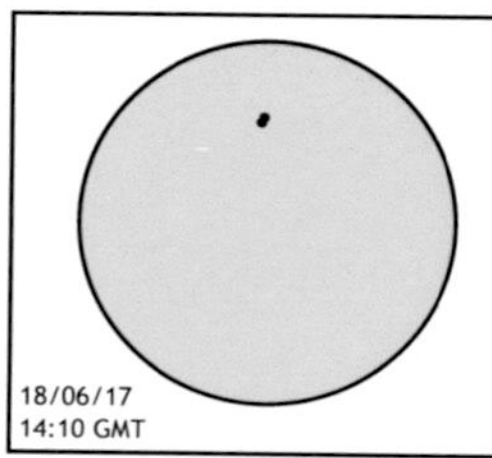

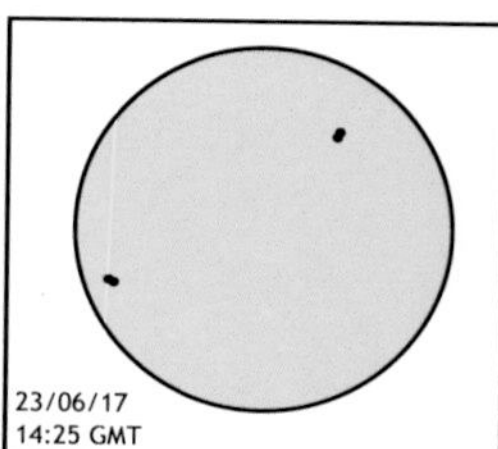

The longitudes of the sunspot (or group) on different dates can then be found with the aid of a transparent grid placed over the solar disc.

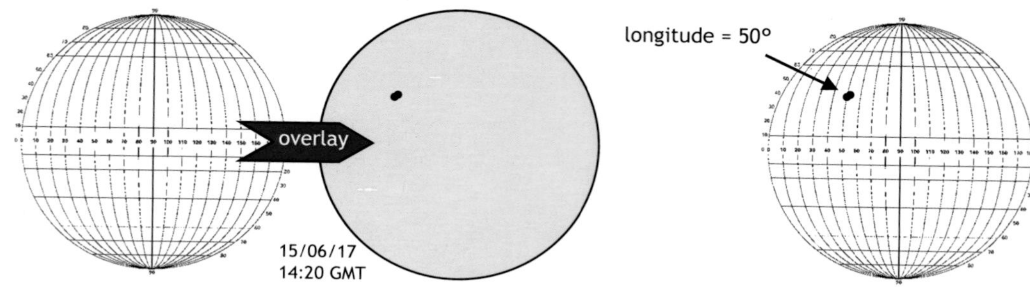

If the difference in longitude (ΔL) of a sunspot (or group) occurs in a time interval Δt, then rotation period (T) can be calculated using the formula:

$$\frac{T}{\Delta t} = \frac{360°}{\Delta L}$$

This can be repeated for different times and longitude differences, from which the mean solar rotation period at the particular latitude can be calculated.

9.2 The Sun's interior

The temperature in the central **core** of the Sun is ~15 million K. This is hot enough for thermonuclear reactions involving the fusion of hydrogen (H) nuclei into helium (He) nuclei to occur (the temperature has to be high to overcome the mutual electrostatic repulsion of the positively-charged nuclei).

The most common series of reactions is called the **proton - proton chain:**

$${}^{1}_{1}\text{H} + {}^{1}_{1}\text{H} \longrightarrow {}^{2}_{1}\text{H} + {}^{0}_{1}\text{e}^{+} + {}^{0}_{0}\nu$$

positron neutrino

$${}^{2}_{1}\text{H} + {}^{1}_{1}\text{H} \longrightarrow {}^{3}_{2}\text{He}$$

$${}^{3}_{2}\text{He} + {}^{3}_{2}\text{He} \longrightarrow {}^{4}_{2}\text{He} + {}^{1}_{1}\text{H} + {}^{1}_{1}\text{H}$$

At each stage in the chain, mass (m) is lost and converted into energy (E) in accordance with Einstein's equation $E = m\,c^2$, where c is the speed of light.

The Sun loses 4 million tonnes of mass every second, but don't worry, that's insignificant compared with the Sun's total mass (2.0×10^{27} tonne).

Immediately above the Sun's core is the **radiative zone** where the energy in the form of photons (gamma-radiation) is transferred (in a rather random manner due to the scattering of photons by electrons) outwards.

The outer ~200 000 km of the Sun is the **convective zone** where thermal energy is transported to the photosphere by rising convection currents of hot plasma. At the base of this zone, the temperature is ~2 million K; at the top - the 100-km thick visible surface or **photosphere** - the temperature is 5800 K.

The *Sun | trek* website is full of information about the Sun and its interactions with Earth. It contains Sun-based projects suitable for all ages using real solar data, and a wealth of resources about the Sun for both pupils and teachers.

www.suntrek.org

9.3 The Sun's atmosphere and the solar wind

The Sun's photosphere radiates energy in the form of visible light and, to a lesser extent, infra-red, ultra-violet and X-radiation.

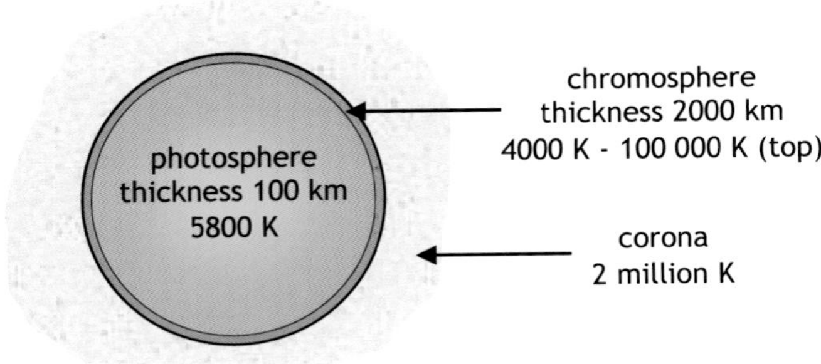

Charged particles of the solar wind ionise gas to produce the ion tail of a comet and cause it to fluoresce. They also constrain the ion tail into a direction away from the Sun.

Image credit: NASA

Above the photosphere, the solar atmosphere consists of the spherical **chromosphere** and the tenuous, sometimes petal-shaped **corona** which extends outwards for millions of km into space. The corona is only visible during a total solar eclipse, as shown in the remarkable photograph by Michael Kobusch.

The Earth has a magnetic field that is similar to that of a simple bar magnet.

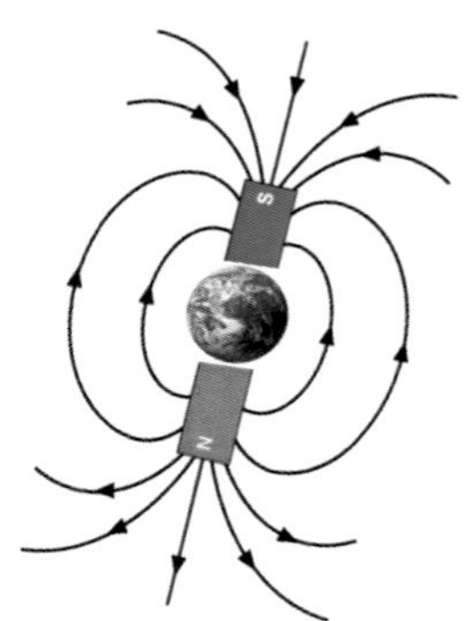

Without the solar wind, the Earth's magnetic field would resemble that of a bar magnet. Instead, its **magnetosphere** is somewhat more complex as shown in this NASA graphic.

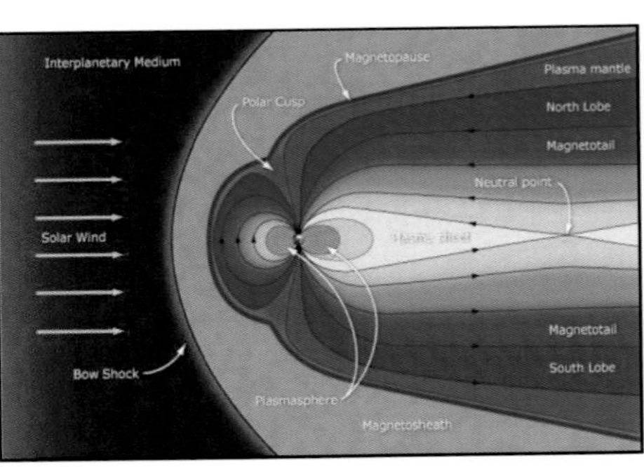

Charged particles of the solar wind are also responsible for creating the breathtaking aurorae.

Image credit: Ole Salomonsen

The 'slow' solar wind is an outflow of charged particles (mostly protons and electrons) from the Sun's corona that are ejected into space at speeds of ~400 km/s. There is also a 'fast' solar wind emitted from **coronal holes** and 'gusts' of radiation associated with **coronal mass ejections** and **solar flares**.

The solar wind is responsible for aurora and the creation, direction and visibility of cometary tails. In addition, it can trigger world-wide geomagnetic storms that cause overloading of power lines, add unwanted 'noise' to radio transmissions, affect the electronic components of instruments on orbiting satellites and add to the radiation risk to astronauts and air passengers.

The Earth - Sun space environment is a fascinating subject in its own right, and we recommend that interested teachers and pupils should explore two further resources: www.spaceweather.com and http://www.swpc.noaa.gov

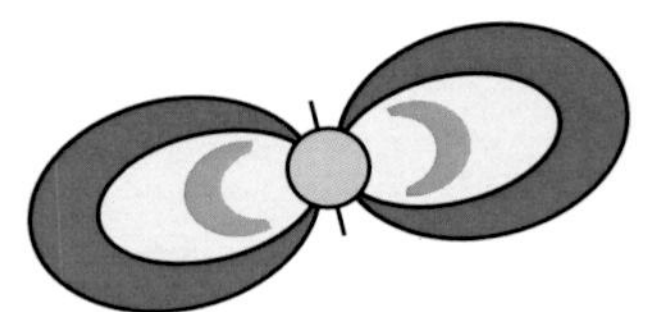

The Van Allen Belts are two doughnut-shaped rings of charged particles trapped in the Earth's magnetic field. The inner belt has an altitude of between 0.1 and 1.5 Earth-radii (1500 km - 10 000 km) and contains mainly protons; the outer belt has an altitude between 3 and 10 Earth-radii (15 000 km - 65 000 km) and contains mainly electrons.

10.1 Tides and precession

10.2 Eclipses

10.3 Sizes and distances

10 The Earth - Moon - Sun system

10.1 Tides and precession

$$F \alpha \frac{M_1 \times M_2}{d^2}$$

Newton's law of universal gravitation can be written in symbols: note in particular the dependence of *F* on the ***inverse*** of ***distance squared***.

In chapter 8 we introduced the ideas that gravitational forces:

- act on bodies with mass (M_1 and M_2), and are responsible for orbital motion;
- obey an inverse square law with distance (d).

We can now study how the second idea gives rise to **tidal forces**. Let's consider a lighter body (such as Jupiter's innermost Galilean moon Io) in orbit around a more massive body (Jupiter).

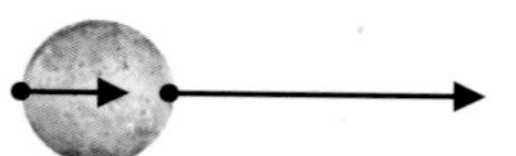

The gravitational pull by Jupiter on Io's near side is greater than its pull on the far side

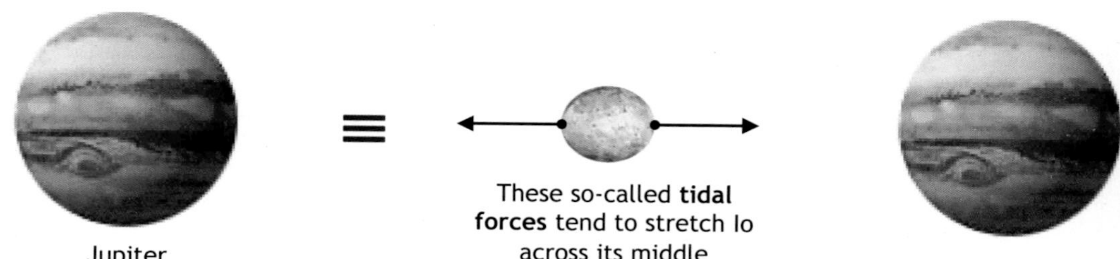

Jupiter

These so-called **tidal forces** tend to stretch Io across its middle

The inverse square nature of the force causes the gravitational pull by Jupiter on Io's near side to be greater than that on its far side (as indicated by the relative lengths of the arrows on the left). This is equivalent to two equal and opposite forces acting on the moon's near and far sides that tend to stretch and elongate Io as shown in the (somewhat exaggerated) diagram on the right.

It is important to point out that Io causes a similar, but weaker, effect on Jupiter.

Now let's apply these ideas to the Earth - Moon system. The Moon exerts similar tidal forces on the near and far sides of the Earth. As with Jupiter's effect on Io, this is equivalent to two equal and opposite forces pulling on the Earth.

The gravitational pull by the Moon on the Earth's near side is greater than its pull on the far side

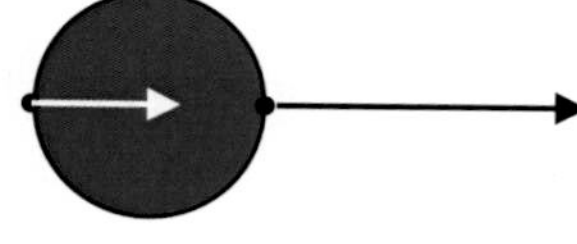

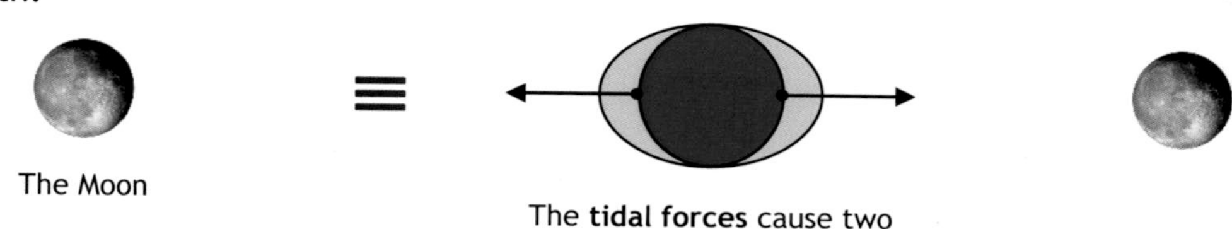

The Moon

The **tidal forces** cause two tidal bulges in the Earth's oceans

These have the effect of creating two **tidal bulges** in the oceans on the parts of the Earth facing towards and away from the Moon. As the Earth spins, parts of the coast experience these bulges as the twice-daily **high** and **low tides**.

Tidal bulges created in the Earth's oceans give us twice-daily high and low tides.

Image by the author

The Sun's gravitational pull also contributes to the tides; at full and new Moon, when the Sun, Earth and Moon are aligned, particularly high and low **spring tides** occur. In between these times, close to when the Moon is half full, the Sun and Moon's tidal forces act at right angles to one another to produce **neap tides** whose height variations are much lower and less dramatic.

A second consequence of the gravitational pull by the Sun and Moon - this time on the slight bulge around the Earth's equator - is the slow wobbling, or **precession**, of the Earth's axis, introduced on page 27.

Evidence for this axial **precession** includes:

- the changing 'Pole Star';
- the changing locations of the equinoxes (the points where the ecliptic crosses the celestial equator): these are slowly drifting westwards so that the First Point of Aries that marks the spring equinox is no longer in the constellation of Aries but rather in Pisces (and heading towards Aquarius);
- the misalignment of ancient monuments and temples: many such structures were carefully aligned to particular stars, and by knowing the rate of precession of the Earth's axis (about 1.4° per century), archaeoastronomers can determine the approximate dates of their construction.

The Earth's precession rate is 1.4° per century.

How many years does it take the Earth's axis to precess by 1.0°?

Answer after Index

10.2 Eclipses

It is an amazing cosmic coincidence that the Sun and Moon appear to be the same size; both angular diameters are roughly 0.5°. When the Moon passes directly in front of the Sun, it obscures light from the photosphere to produce a stunning **total solar eclipse** for observers in the dark shadow (**umbra**) on Earth.

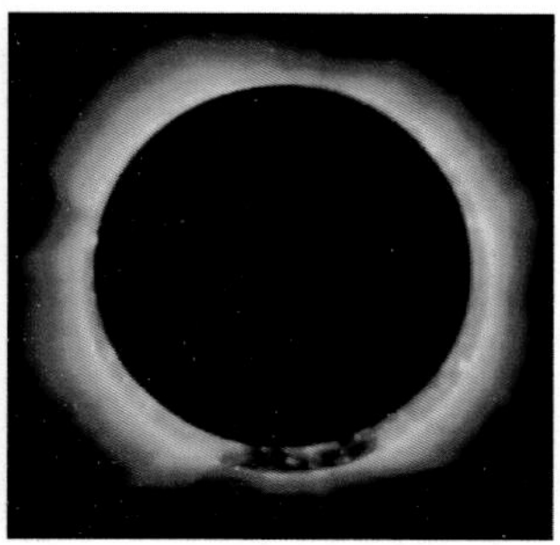

Left: a spectacular annular solar eclipse in which most (but not all) of the photosphere is covered by the Moon. Middle: a partial solar eclipse in which only a portion of the Moon covers the Sun's disc. Right: A total lunar eclipse.

Image credits: www.space.com, David Reneke and John W. Johnson

The Diamond Ring effect is caused by light from the Sun shinning through valleys on the Moon. It can occur just before or after totality.

Image credit: David Cornfield/MIT

During totality the sky darkens, some stars can be seen, the temperature drops and the Sun's corona can be seen. Just before and after totality, small bright spots of sunlight caused by the Sun's rays shining through valleys on the Moon are visible. These are called **Baily's Beads**, and when only one is visible, this is known as the **Diamond Ring** effect.

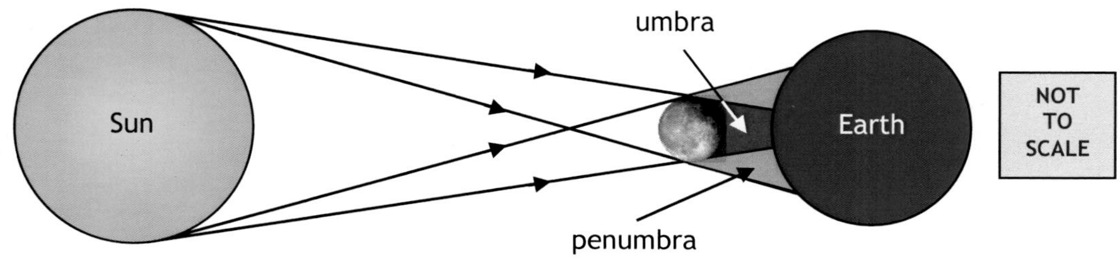

Solar eclipses occur at new Moon and last for a few minutes. If the Moon obscures just part of the Sun - the observer is located in the **penumbra** - then the Sun appears to only have a small 'bite' out of it: a **partial solar eclipse**.

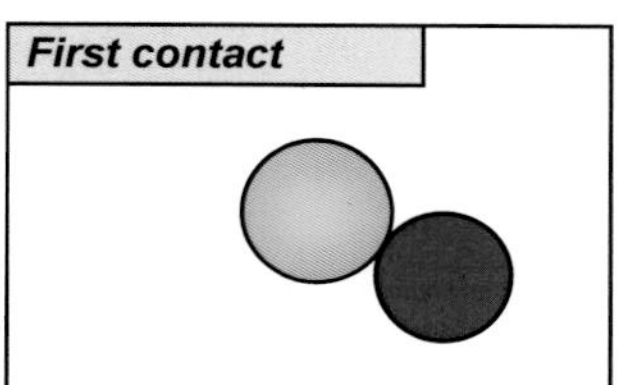

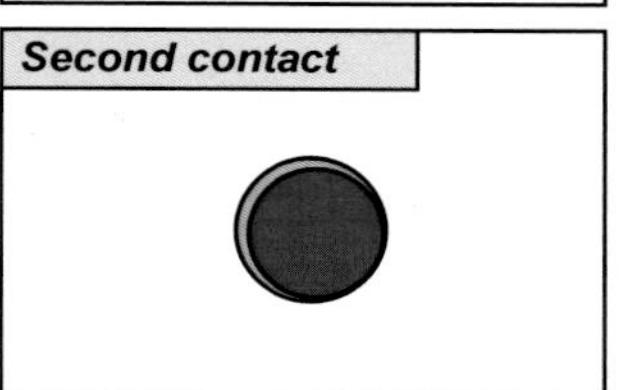

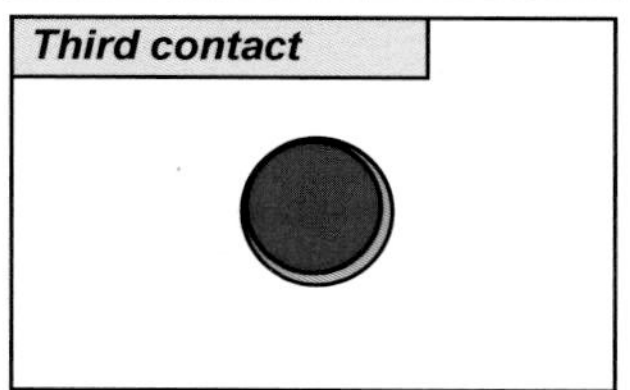

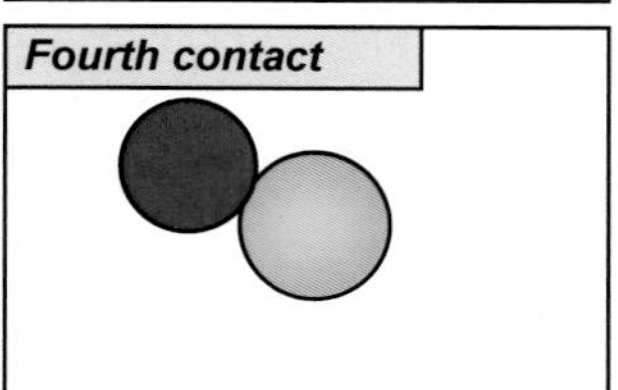

The sequence shows the progress of an annular solar eclipse, from first contact to fourth contact.

The same terminology applies to a ***total*** solar eclipse

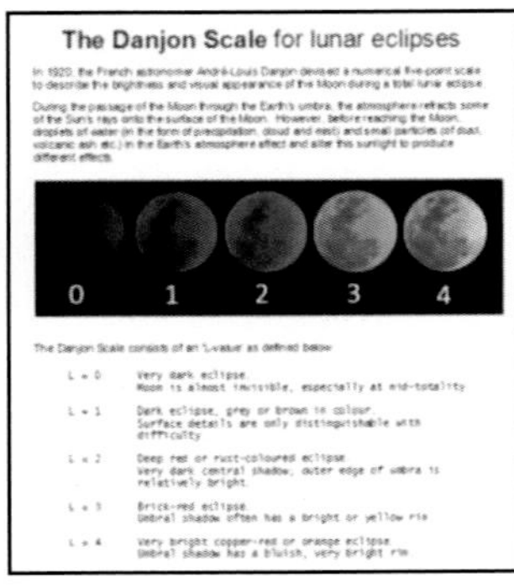

The **Danjon Scale** can be used to estimate the colour of a total lunar eclipse.

The *New Pupil Toolkit for GCSE (9-1) Astronomy* contains explanatory notes on this and lots of other topics.

An **annular eclipse** is a special kind of partial solar eclipse in which the Moon's silhouetted disc is slightly smaller than at other times; this is due to the Moon being close to apogee in its elliptical orbit around the Earth. The Sun appears as a thin annulus or 'ring of fire', when otherwise it would be totally obscured.

The progress of a total or annular eclipse is marked by four (umbral) 'contacts' (between the Moon's and the Sun's discs) as shown on the previous page.

Lunar eclipses occur when the Moon passes through the Earth's (umbral, for a total eclipse or penumbral/part-umbral, for a partial eclipse) shadow. They occur at full Moon, and during totality the Moon is copper/rusty-red in colour due to predominantly red light refracting through the Earth's atmosphere - the blue light has already been scattered - and illuminating the Moon.

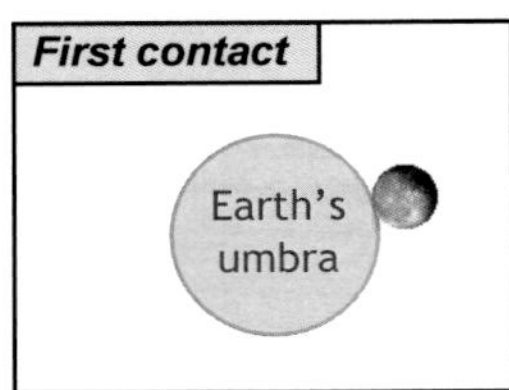

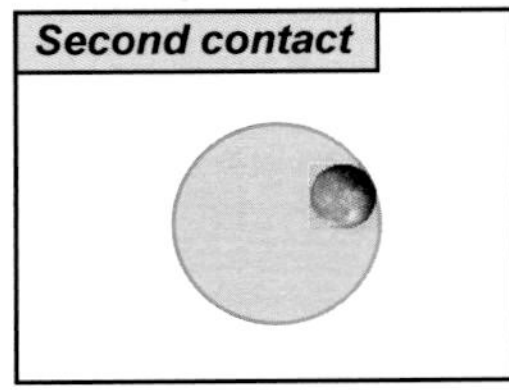

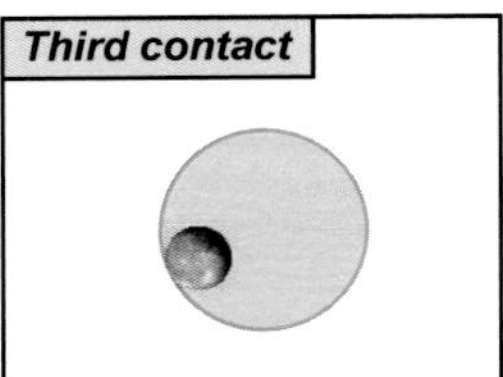

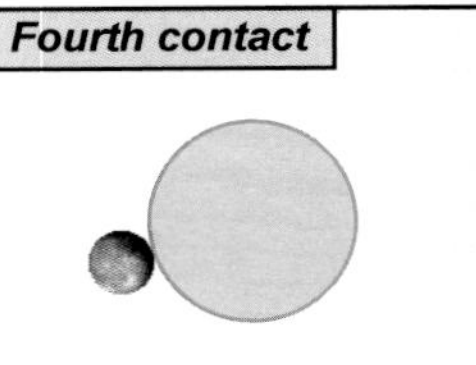

A partial lunar eclipse, in which only part of the Moon passes through the Earth's umbra and the remainder crosses the penumbra.

Once again, key points in the eclipse's progress are described as first - fourth umbral contacts.

Whereas the time interval between second and third contact is only a few minutes for a solar eclipse, the time interval between second and third umbral contact for a lunar eclipse is much longer - up to 3 hours - because of the larger size of the Earth's shadow compared with that of the Moon.

10.3 Sizes and distances

Over 2200 years ago, the ancient Greeks were able to apply their geometrical skills, supported by a few simple assumptions, to crude measurements of lengths, angles and time intervals to determine first the **scale**, and then the **size**, of the Earth - Moon - Sun system.

Two Greeks in particular were responsible for establishing the first rungs on the so-called 'cosmic distance ladder': Eratosthenes and Aristarchus of Samos.

Eratosthenes (*c.* 276-196 BCE) used shadows and (perhaps) an army of men to determine the circumference of the Earth to amazing accuracy (probably)

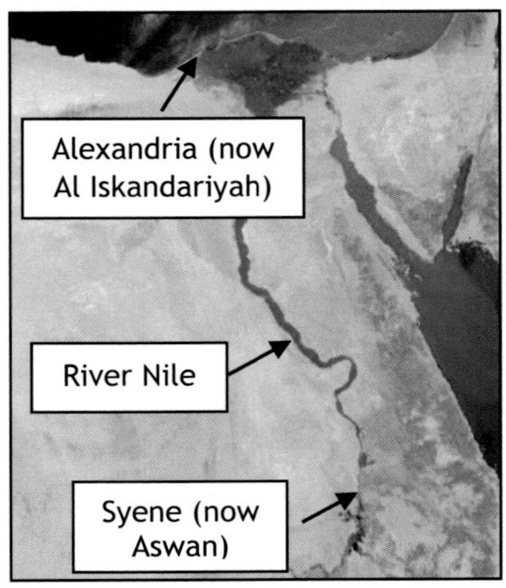

Multi-talented Eratosthenes was in charge of the Great Library of Alexandria (which is now Al Iskandariyah) in Egypt.

It came to his attention that at noon on the date of the summer solstice (June 21st), the Sun lay directly over a deep well in the city of Syene (now Aswan) which was some distance to the south on the Tropic of Cancer; in addition, there were no shadows cast by obelisks and pillars at that time.

These observations implied that the Sun was directly overhead in Syene.

The number of specific points made in students' 'extended writing' answers should closely match the number of marks indicated in the question.

At the same time in Alexandria, however, the Sun was ***not*** directly overhead: vertical poles and columns ***did*** cast a shadow, and Eratosthenes sought to use such a pole to determine the angle between the Sun and the vertical.

By measuring the height of his pole and the length of its shadow at noon, Eratosthenes was able to calculate angle A; its value was 'one fiftieth of a circle', or just over 7°.

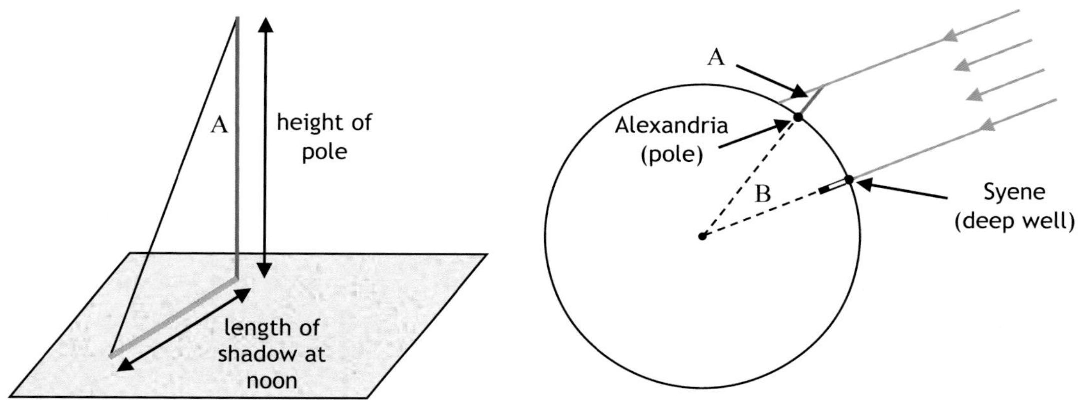

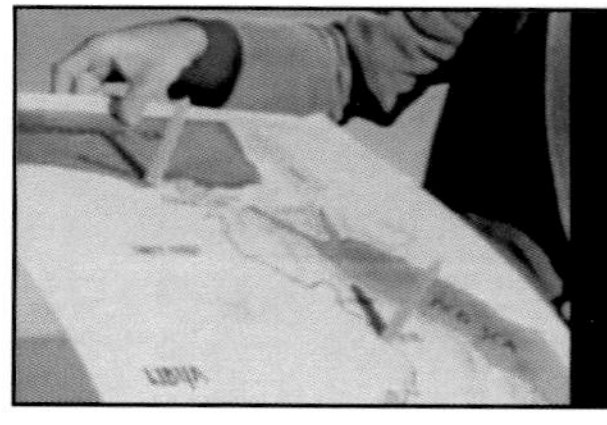

There's an excellent *YouTube* clip presented by astronomer Carl Sagan about Eratosthenes and how he determined the Earth's circumference:

https://www.youtube.com/watch?v=G8cblWMv0rI

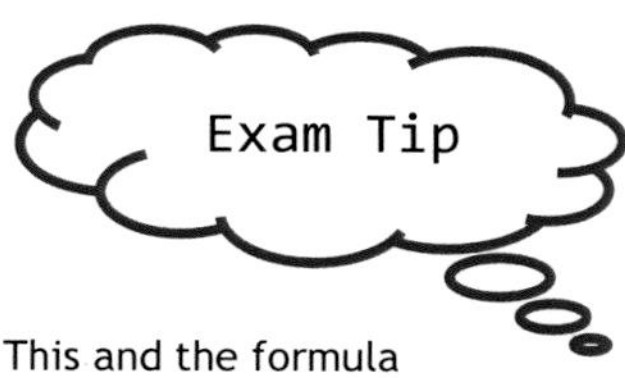

This and the formula for the relative diameters of the Earth and Moon (below) won't be given in examination papers, so students will need to ***understand how and when to use them***.

Assuming that the Sun was so distant that its rays of light were parallel, Eratosthenes used a diagram similar to the one above (right) to show that angles A and B were alternate angles and therefore equal to each other.

He then calculated the circumference of the Earth using the proportion:

$$\frac{\text{circumference of Earth}}{\text{distance from Syene to Alexandria}} = \frac{360°}{7°}$$

We don't know how Eratosthenes 'measured' the distance between Alexandria and Syene. Some sources say that he employed an army of men to pace it out and others say that he counted the number of rotations of a wheel of a carriage that was driven between the two cities.

Whatever the method of measuring the distance between Alexandria and Syene, Eratosthenes arrived at a value close to 5000 *stadia*. The Greek *stadion* (Latin *stadium*) was the ancient Greeks' unit of length; one *stadium* was the length of a straight running track, but a standard length for the *stadium* did not exist (its modern-day value is ~180 m). Amazingly, Eratosthenes' accuracy in determining the Earth's circumference was probably less than 10%. Just using sticks!

The relative diameter of the Moon compared with that of the Earth was determined by Aristarchus of Samos. He observed a total lunar eclipse and assumed that:

- a lunar eclipse was produced when the Moon passed into the Earth's umbra;
- the Sun was so far away that its rays were parallel when reaching the Earth;
- the Moon's path took it through the centre of the Earth's umbra which had the same diameter as that of the Earth.

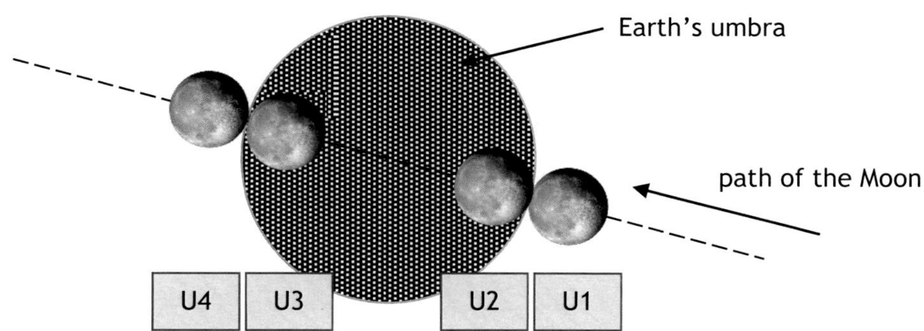

Aristarchus of Samos (*c*. 310-230 BCE) timed lunar eclipses, used crude protractors (probably) and the width of his thumb at arm's length to calculate the distances to, and diameters of, two of our closest neighbours in space.

With all three of the assumptions met, Aristarchus showed that:

$$\frac{\text{diameter of Moon}}{\text{diameter of Earth}} = \frac{\text{time interval from U1 to U2}}{\text{time interval from U2 to U4}}$$

The table gives the times (GMT) of first - fourth umbral contacts for a total lunar eclipse:

umbral contact	time (GMT)
first	17:57
second	19:30
third	22:35
fourth	00:08

Use these data to calculate the ratio of the diameter of the Earth : diameter of the Moon to the nearest whole number.

State one important assumption that you have made.

Answers after Index

The Moon at first quarter...or is it slightly before...or slightly after? Even today, it is difficult to judge when precisely half of the Moon is illuminated and difficult to determine the Sun - Earth - Moon angle.

Although Aristarchus' value for the ratio of the Sun's and Moon's distances from us was inaccurate, the method that he employed was nevertheless very sound.

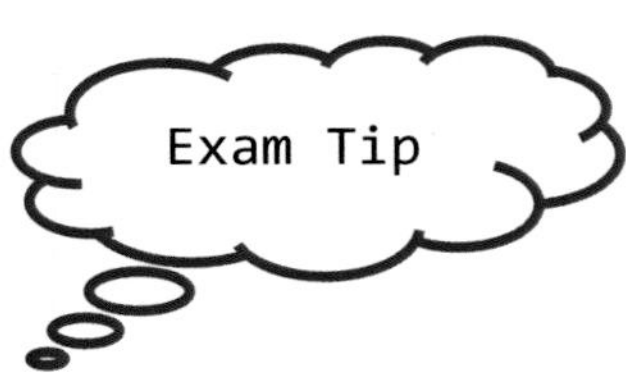

When students are calculating time intervals such as in the Pop Quiz question on this page, it is important to note that times are given in ***hours : minutes*** and **NOT** ***decimal hours***.

Aristarchus was able to calculate that the Moon's diameter was 'between 0.32 and 0.40 times that of the Earth'. The correct value is 0.27 times that of the Earth.

Combining this with Eratosthenes' value for the circumference (and hence diameter) of the Earth, it was possible to calculate the diameter of the Moon.

The Greeks then set about determining the distance to the Moon. Aristarchus reckoned that when he held his thumb at arm's length, it was just able to cover the Moon's disc.

A pupil estimates the apparent size of the Sun (partly obscured by clouds for safety reasons) by comparing it with the size of her thumb held at arm's length.

By measuring the width of his thumb and the length of his outstretched arm, Aristarchus obtained a value for the angular size of his thumb and hence that of the Moon. A knowledge of triangles - 'real' trigonometry was yet to be invented - then allowed Aristarchus to calculate the Earth - Moon distance.

A further ingenious method allowed Aristarchus to determine the relative distances of the Sun and Moon. He waited until the Moon was exactly in its first quarter phase and measured the angle between the Moon and the Sun.

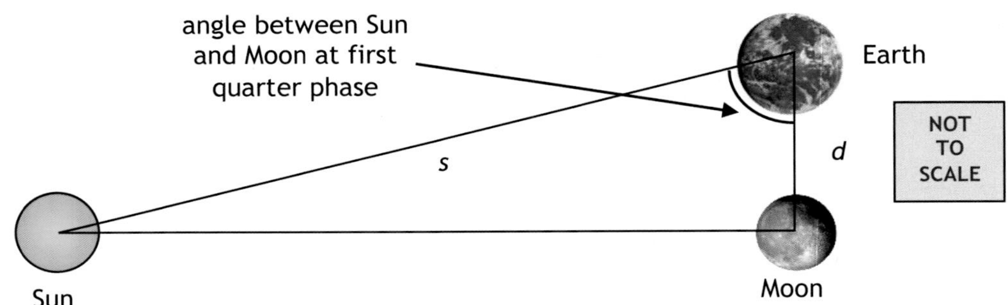

It is uncertain how Aristarchus measured this angle, but we do know that he obtained a value of '29/30 of a right angle' which equates to 87°. Using his knowledge of triangles, Aristarchus determined the radio s / d to be 'between 18 and 20': the Sun was about 20 times more distant than the Moon.

We now know that the ratio is close to 400, and suggest that the error was mainly due to the difficulty in measuring an angle that was very close to 90°.

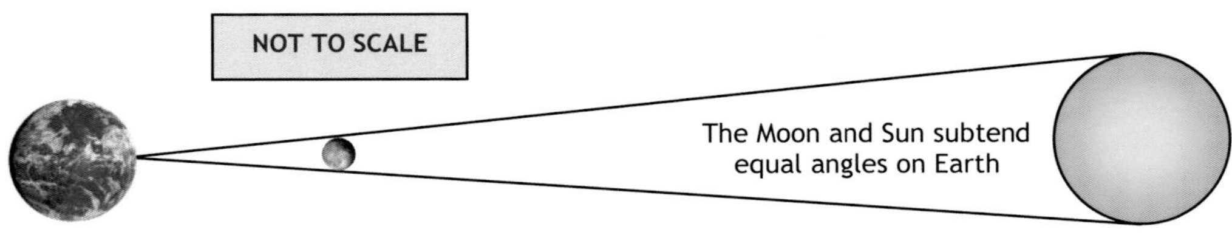

The Greeks knew that the Sun and Moon subtended the same angle: if the Sun was 20 times further away than the Moon, its diameter must be 20 times larger.

Knowing the diameter of the Moon (from earlier calculations), the diameter of the Sun could then be calculated.

11 Time and the Earth - Moon - Sun cycles

11.1 Sidereal and synodic time

'Time is an illusion. Lunchtime doubly so.'

Douglas Adams, author

Let us begin this chapter by refreshing our memory on a few key points:

- One **year** corresponds to one complete orbit of the Earth around the Sun;
- During this time, the Earth spins on its axis 365¼ times;
- One **sidereal day** corresponds to the time taken for the Earth to spin once on its axis: it is equal to 23 h 56 min;
- One **solar** or **synodic day** is 4 min longer: 24 h 00 min;

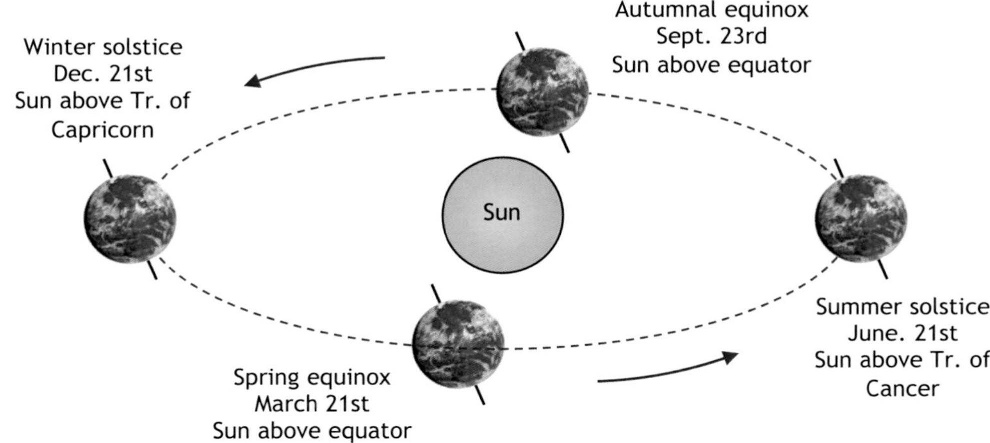

- Ignoring precession (see page 27), the Earth's axis of rotation remains fixed with respect to the stars, but it is ***not*** fixed with respect to the Sun;
- During one solar orbit, the Sun lies directly above key latitudes on key dates (shown above: the exact dates can vary by ± 2 days).

The Earth's orbit around the Sun and its fixed axis of rotation explain why the Sun rises and sets at different times on different dates during the year. It also explains the apparent motion of the Sun on the celestial sphere (see page 26) and why the altitude of the Sun at noon is different on different dates.

Close to the spring and autumn equinoxes, the days and nights are roughly the same length. (There's a clue in the name: the Latin word *equinoctial* translates as 'equal night'.) As spring advances, the days become longer with the times of sunrise and sunset being gradually earlier and later in the day.

The Sun rises at its earliest and sets at its latest times on dates close to the summer solstice in June; in December, close to the date of the winter solstice, the reverse is true. In the southern hemisphere, the opposite applies: days are longer in December and shorter in June.

12:00 am/pm

Contrary to popular (and incorrect) opinion, there are no such times as 12:00 am and 12:00 pm: they are 12:00 noon and 12:00 midnight.

In the UK, the Sun is low over the southern horizon at noon on December 21st (the date of the winter solstice)...

...but on June 21st (the date of the summer solstice), the altitude of the Sun at noon is 47° higher.

What is the astronomical significance of the 47°?

Answer after Index

A waxing gibbous Moon. Note the contrast in features located near the **terminator** due to the low angle of the Sun in the lunar sky near the terminator.

Image by the author

11.2 Lunar phases

Image credit: NASA

The sequence of images (from top left to bottom right) shows the lunar phase cycle.

Following new Moon, the lunar disc shows a very thin crescent phase that waxes to become half full and gibbous, eventually becoming a full Moon.

The Moon then wanes through its gibbous, half-full and (de)crescent phases.

'Once in a Blue Moon'

This common phrase that refers to a rare event probably has an astronomical origin.

A 'Blue Moon' refers to the second full Moon in a calendar month.

Although one **sidereal month** - the time for one complete revolution of the Earth - is equivalent to 27.3 days, one **solar (synodic) month** - the lunar phase cycle (shown above) - is 2.2 days longer: 29.5 days.

The reason for this difference is that during the time taken for the Moon to complete one orbit of the Earth, the Earth - Moon system has moved through an angle of 27° in its orbit around the Sun.

At position M_1 the Moon is aligned with the Sun and Earth (New Moon).

During one complete orbit (27.3 days), the Moon has moved from position M_1 to M_2.

During this time, the Earth has moved significantly in its solar orbit from E_1 to E_2.

An extra 2.2 days are needed to re-align the Moon (now at M_3) with the Sun and Earth once more.

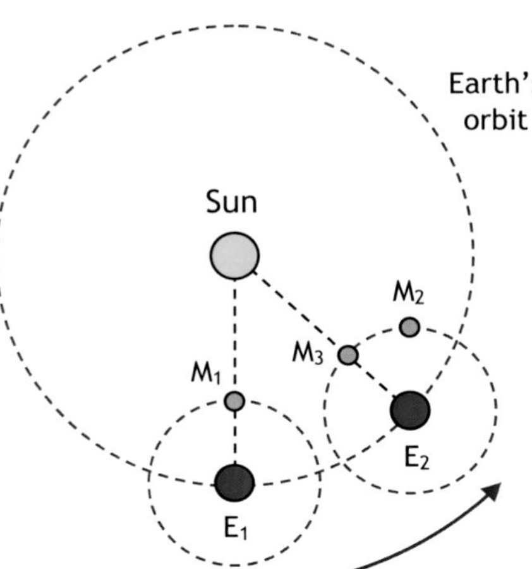

Which calendar month can never contain a Blue Moon?

11.3 Sundials and shadow sticks

A horizontal sundial in which the gnomon (which points to the North Celestial Pole) casts a shadow onto the dial plate.

Image by the author

Sundials and shadow sticks use an opaque object to cast a shadow of the Sun.

In the case of a **sundial**, the object is traditionally a metallic triangular gnomon whose slanting edge points to the North Celestial Pole (NCP). The shadow is cast onto a horizontal plate that contains the graduated scale from which the time can be read.

A vertical sundial on the west face of St. Margaret's Church in Central London; the gnomon (marked by the stars) also points to the NCP.

Image by the author

Sundials have been used to tell the time since antiquity. When correctly aligned, they indicate **Apparent Solar Time** (**AST**). However, whereas our phones, watches and Town Hall clocks tick evenly by the same amount every second of the day, the Sun does not oblige us with such regularity: on some days the Sun moves more slowly across the sky, on others it moves more quickly for reasons we will see below.

So, in the days before we had such time-keeping devices, a correction had to be made to the Apparent Solar Time as indicated on a sundial in order to obtain the **Mean Solar Time** (**MST**) for a particular location. This was based on an imaginary **Mean Sun** that ***did*** cross the sky in a consistent manner.

The correction is known as the **Equation of Time (EOT)** and its value - this can be negative as well as positive - differs for different dates of the year.

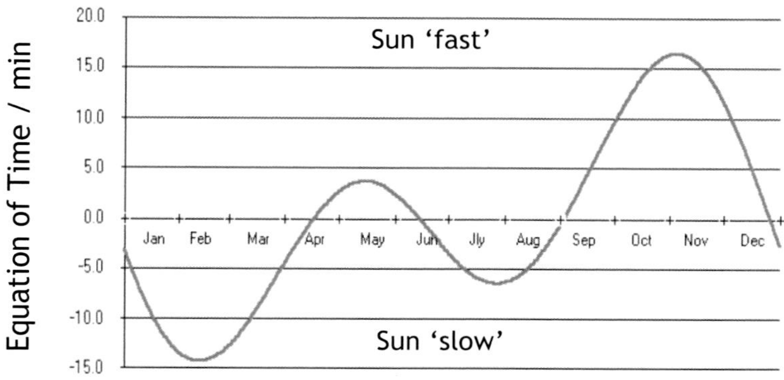

Equation of Time (EOT) = Apparent Solar Time (AST) - Mean Solar Time (MST)

When the EOT is positive, we say that the real Sun is 'fast' (i.e. faster than the Mean Sun) and when the EOT is negative, we say that the real Sun is 'slow'.

So, using simple arithmetic, if a sundial reads 10:45 on a particular day of the year and the EOT for that date is -5 min, then the Mean Solar Time is 10:50.

As the name suggests, a **shadow stick** often uses a vertical, wooden, circular and reasonably thin stick such as 1-cm diameter dowel, often placed in a bucket or plant pot of sand or gravel, to cast its shadow onto a large horizontal piece of light-coloured card. It can be used to determine the time at which the Sun culminates (at local noon) ***and*** the observer's longitude.

As the Sun rises in the east, culminates when due south and stars to set in the west, the length and direction of the shadow will change.

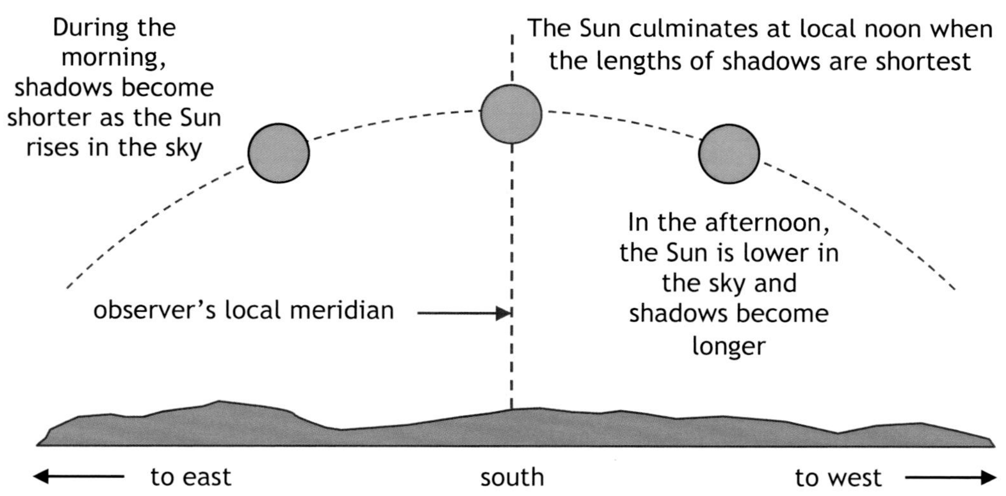

Full details on how to carry out this experiment are included in our *New Pupil Toolkit for GCSE (9-1) Astronomy*, but basically the tip of the shadow should be marked with a small cross every, say, five minutes from about 10:30 until 13:30 (or 11:30 until 14:30 in the summer when Daylight Saving Time applies) together with the time indicated by a phone or watch.

True or False?

a) In February, the Sun moves across the sky more slowly than the Mean Sun.

b) In July, the Apparent Solar Time is always later than the Mean Solar Time.

c) In October, the Mean Sun is always ahead of the real Sun.

d) On four dates of the year, the EOT is zero.

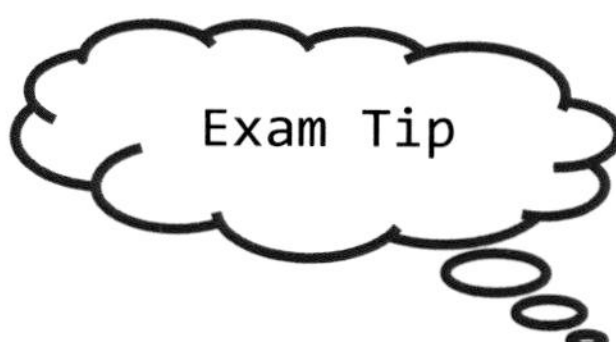

Students should be able to rearrange this formula and deduce the value of the EOT from tables and graphs in order to obtain a value for either AST or MST.

An impressive vertical sundial on the wall of Pembroke College, Cambridge.

Note the graphical version of the Equation of Time displayed below the sundial.

Image credit: Ian Nash

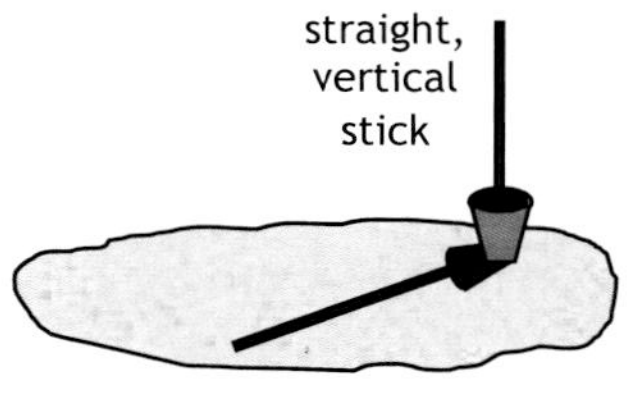

A simple shadow stick can be used to determine the time of local noon and the longitude from where the experiment is carried out.

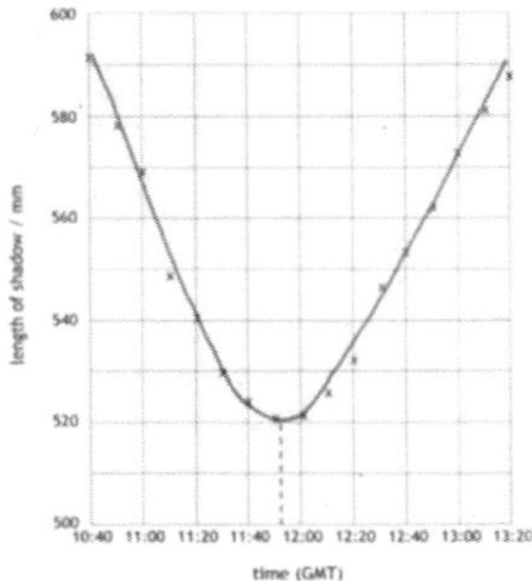

By drawing a line-of-best-fit through the points, the time corresponding to the bottom of the curve (the time of the shortest shadow) can be deduced.

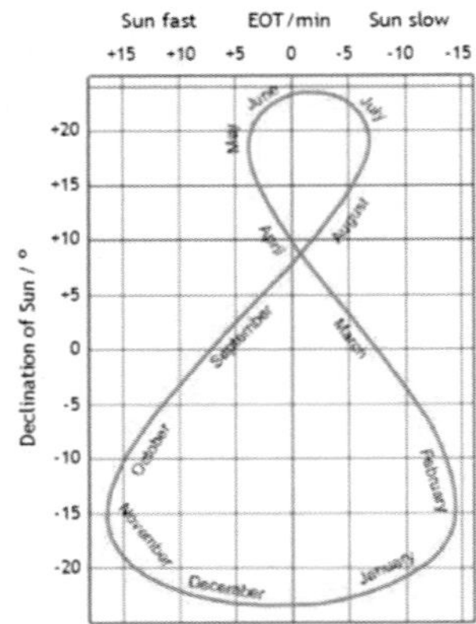

An analemma is a chart showing how the EOT varies with the Sun's declination during the course of one year.

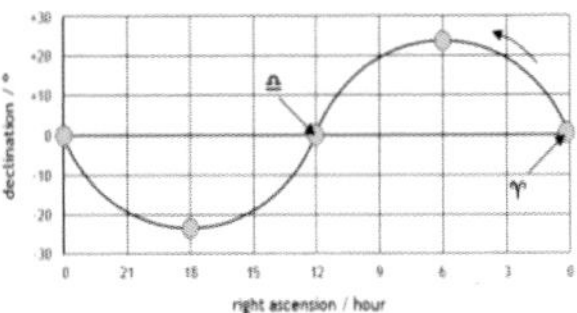

The real Sun moves up, down and eastwards along the curved ***ecliptic*** during the course of one year, but the Mean Sun moves eastwards along the ***celestial equator*** during the year.

Unaided observational tasks A9 and A10 both involve using shadows (cast by a shadow stick and a sundial gnomon respectively) to determine longitude and assess the accuracy of a sundial.

Once the length of the stick's shadow at different times around local noon have been found, a graph of shadow length against time indicated on a watch or phone can be plotted. It is important that the shadow length-axis does not start at zero since the 'curve' will be vary shallow - but avoid zigzags - and this will make it difficult to judge the lowest point on the curve.

The graph should be a smooth curve - don't join the dots - from which the time of the shortest shadow can be read off on the time-axis; the graph indicates that this occurred at 11:52 civil time (GMT).

11.4 The Equation of Time

In addition to tables and graphs such as the one on the previous page, the EOT can also be read from an **analemma**. This has been likened by many students to a 'wobbly snowman' and shows how the EOT varies with month of the year and also the Sun's decimation. Charts, graphs and analemmae show that:

- from late December until mid-April, the EOT is negative by up to 14 min; the Sun (in the sky) is slow compared with the Mean Sun;
- from mid-April until the middle of June, the EOT is positive by up to 4 min; the Sun is fast;
- from the middle of June until the beginning of September, the EOT is negative again by up to 7 min; the Sun is slow again;
- from early September until late December, the EOT is positive by up to 17 min; the real Sun in the sky is fast again.

In winter, the Sun is slow (EOT negative)

In spring, the Sun is fast (EOT positive)

In summer, the Sun is slow (EOT negative)

In autumn, the Sun is fast (EOT positive)

Earlier we introduced the concept of the Mean Sun which forms the basis of civil (as opposed to solar) timekeeping. The Mean Sun moves across the sky - more precisely, on the celestial equator - at a fixed rate every day. The real Sun, however, moves up, down and along the ecliptic at different rates, and so the annual variation in the EOT is due to two factors:

- the Earth's **elliptical orbit**: the Earth travels at different speeds in its orbit, causing the real Sun to move slower or faster in the sky on different dates;
- the **tilt of the Earth's axis** or **obliquity of the ecliptic**: close to the solstices, the real Sun is travelling faster from east to west than when close to the equinoxes when a large component of its apparent 'motion' is northwards or southwards; the Sun therefore lags behind and leaps ahead of the Mean Sun in its east - west motion.

11.5 Longitude and time zones

We can now return to our shadow stick experiment to show how the data can be used to determine longitude.

Since the shadow data were obtained using the real Sun in the sky, then the local Apparent Solar Time of the shortest shadow was 12:00 noon.

We can now use the Equation of Time to convert AST into local MST; this is also known as **Local Mean Time (LMT)**. Let's say that on the date that we obtained the data, the EOT was +12 min:

$$\text{EOT} = \text{AST} - \text{MST}$$

Rearranging, $\text{MST} = \text{AST} - \text{EOT}$

Substituting, $= 12{:}00 - 12 \text{ min}$

$= 11{:}48.$

So the Local Mean Time was 11:48 and yet the Local Mean Time in Greenwich (i.e. civil time as indicated on a watch) was 11:52, 4 minutes later.

Remembering that the Earth rotates on its axis by 1° every 4 minutes, this means that the difference in longitude between where the experiment was carried out and Greenwich (longitude = 0°) is 1°. Since local noon occurred 4 minutes ***earlier*** than at Greenwich, the longitude from where the experiment was carried out must be ***west*** of Greenwich: longitude = 1° W.

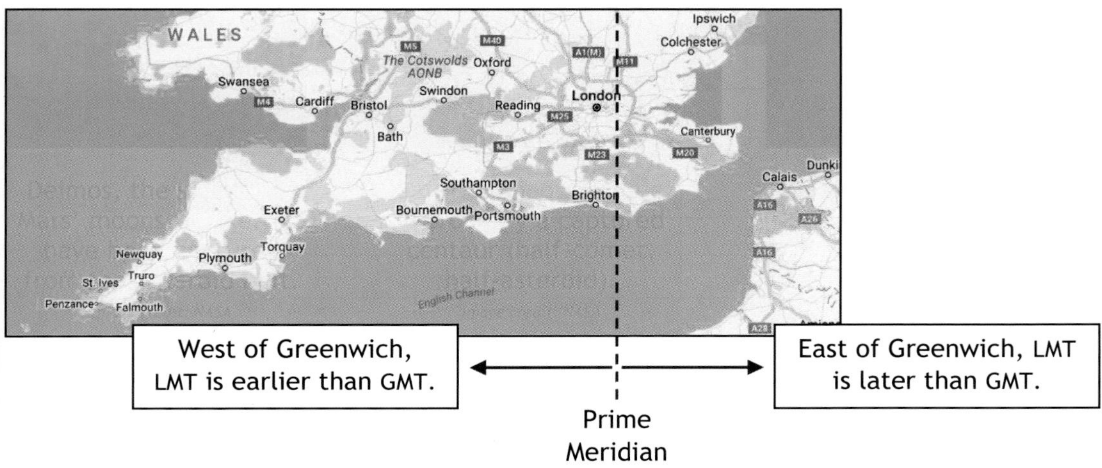

Before rail travel became popular in the second quarter of the 19th century, Local Mean Time was used by all people. Unfortunately, Local Mean Time differed from city to city because the Sun crossed their meridians at slightly different times. This caused a huge problem for railway timetabling until 1847 when the railway companies agreed to use a standard time for all rail journeys.

Finally in 1880, a government legislation standardized time (Local Mean Solar Time at Greenwich, or **Greenwich Mean Time**) for the whole of the country (albeit not without strong resistance by some towns and cities).

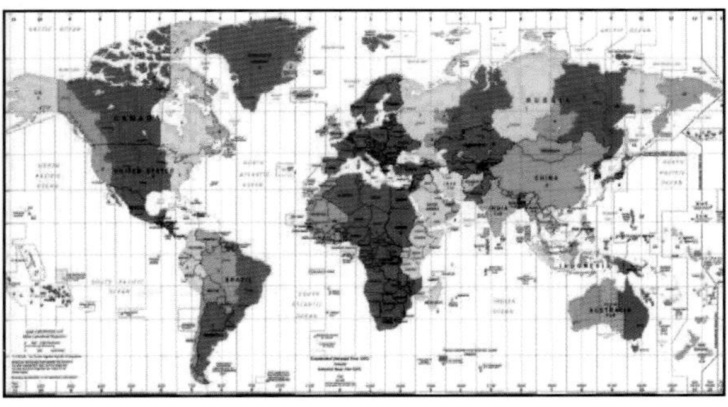

A world map showing the different time zones (*courtesy of ConvertIt.com*).

Since the Earth rotates by 15° in one hour, time zones are roughly 15° wide and most adjacent zones differ in time by 1 hour.

There are, however, some notable exceptions to this generalisation!

Presently, other countries followed suit. We now have a world split into time zones, the majority of which are nominally 15° of longitude wide, with most adjacent zones differing in time by 1 hour (1 hour ≡ 15° Earth-rotation).

Wendy and Joe are communicating via *Instagram* at different locations.

Joe texts a message to Wendy to say his local mean time is 19:40.

Wendy knows that her local mean time is 21:20.

Who is further west and by how many degrees of longitude?

The *Essential Maths Skills for GCSE (9-1) Astronomy* CD-ROM includes in-depth tutorials, worked examples and over 800 practice questions on all the mathematical topics contained in the GCSE (9-1) Astronomy specification, including Time and the determination of longitude.

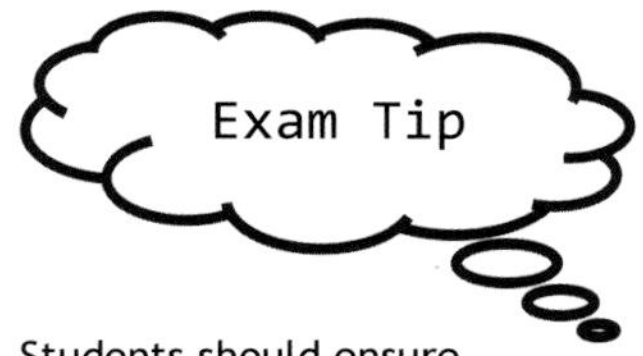

Students should ensure that they are able to quickly 'convert' between the rotation of the Earth (differences in longitude) and time.

For example 1 h ≡ 15°, 20 min ≡ 5° and 4 min ≡ 1°.

An impressive set of clocks in the reception of this hotel in Moscow displays the local time at different world locations, including New York, Hong Kong and London.

Image by the author

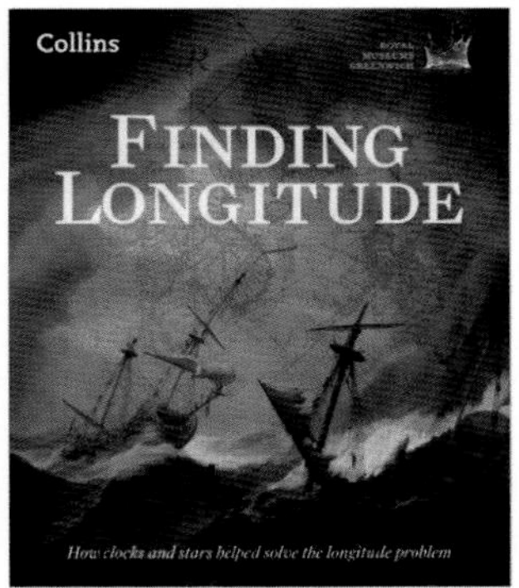

Finding Longitude is a superb illustrated account of how 'astronomers and clockmakers' were able to eventually solve the problem of obtaining an accurate value for a ship's longitude at sea.

'I must go down to the seas again, to the lonely sea and the sky,
And all I ask is a tall ship, and a star to steer her by...'

John Masefield, poet

The 17th century witnessed a rapid expansion in the number of sea vessels exploring or conquering new territories, waging war and trading gold, silk, spices and other such communities with distant lands.

Whereas latitude could be determined easily - even from the deck of a rolling ship - by measuring the altitude of a particular star such as Polaris or the Sun at local noon, longitude posed a huge problem for sea-farers. This inadequacy resulted in numerous shipwrecks and many fatalities.

The longitude problem

In theory, finding longitude at sea is a simple process:

Local Mean Time aboard ship can be determined from observations of the Sun or stars.

This can then be compared with the Local Mean Time in the ship's home port (or some other reference point) and the difference in local time equated to a difference in longitude (1 hour ≡ 15° difference in longitude).

Determining local time in the ship's home port proved the stumbling block to solving the longitude problem.

Left: *Wreck of the 'Amsterdam' c.*1630, artist unknown. Right: *A Fishing Boat Off a Rocky Coast with a Wreck c.*1665, Jacob Adriaensz Bellevois. *Image credits: NMM*

In 1675, King Charles II founded the Royal Observatory in Greenwich with the intention of solving the 'longitude problem'. He learnt that a Frenchman named Le Sieur de St Pierre had resurrected an earlier (1514) proposal by German astronomer Johannes Werner to produce detailed maps showing the position of the Moon at different times and on different dates at some key port.

The intention was that the port's longitude would act as the 0° reference point. This **lunar distance method** allowed a ship's navigator to deduce the local times aboard ship (by observing the stars) ***and*** at his home port (using the maps): the time difference could then be equated to the ship's longitude.

Unfortunately, neither the positions of the stars were well-known nor the motion of the Moon was fully understood. However, the longitude problem was not long from being eventually solved - by 'astronomers and clockmakers'.

The *Time and Longitude* Gallery at the Royal Observatory Greenwich.

On display are John Harrison's rather cumbersome but impressive forerunners (H1, H2 and H3) to what would eventually solve the longitude problem, the pocket watch-sized H4 marine chronometer.

Image credit: Royal Observatory Greenwich

John Harrison's H4 marine chronometer won him the 'Longitude Prize' for successfully keeping accurate time aboard sailing ships.

In 1761, after many trials and tribulations, horologist John Harrison solved the longitude problem with the invention and production of the **marine chronometer** that kept accurate home-port time aboard ships sailing in the most extreme conditions of temperature, humidity and salinity.

12 Formation of planetary systems

12.1 The Solar System: planets and moons

4.6 billion years ago, the nascent Sun was surrounded by a chaotic, swirling **protoplanetary disc** of material comprising approximately 75% hydrogen, 23% helium and 2% other elements such as oxygen, silicon, carbon, iron and nickel. As the distance from the Sun increased, the temperature in the disc decreased.

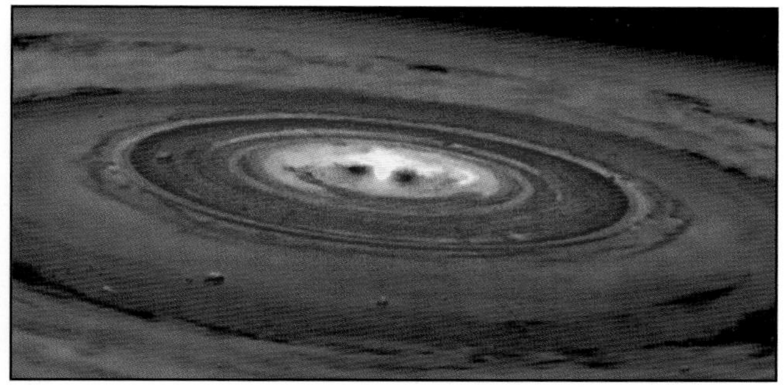

An artist's impression of the protoplanetary disc of left-over material surrounding the (central) newly-formed Sun

Image credit: The Open University

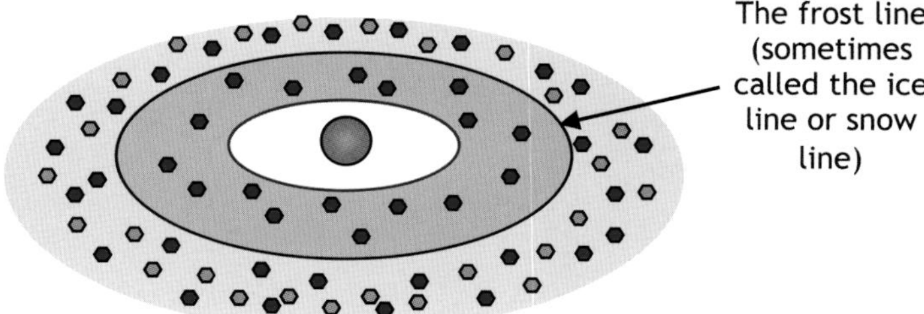

Within the frost line, only metals and silicates (rock) ⬢ were able to condense into small grains; beyond the frost line, it was cold enough for water, carbon dioxide, methane, ammonia and other 'volatiles' ⬡ to be able to condense into solid 'ices'.

At a distance of ~5 AU from the Sun, a **frost line** marked the boundary beyond which it was cold enough for volatile compounds such as water, methane and carbon dioxide to freeze onto tiny particles of dust; within the frost line - but not ***too*** close to the Sun - only metals and rock could condense into solid grains.

Terrestrial planet Mercury was formed ***within*** the frost line; it has a large iron core and rocky surface, but practically no atmosphere due to its high surface temperature and low gravitational field strength.

Hydrogen and helium remained gaseous everywhere; large amounts were 'blown' outwards by the force of the solar wind into the outer Solar System.

The planets formed by **accretion** in which small grains of solid material collided and stuck together forming larger flakes. These in turn collided and stuck to other flakes, eventually forming larger and larger bodies. After an estimated ~ 100 million years, this accumulated material formed the metallic and silicate cores of the planets.

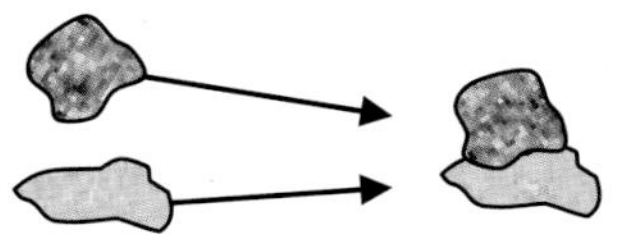
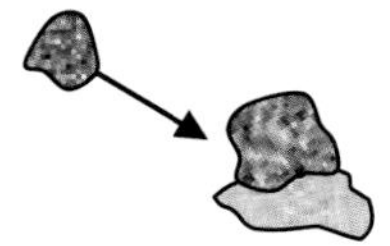
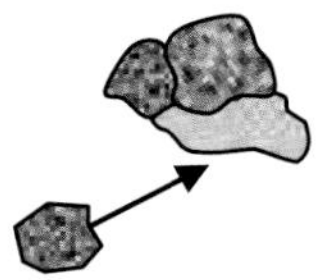
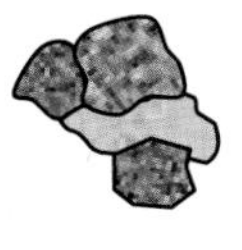

A left-to-right time sequence illustrating the slow, but steady, accretion of tiny grains and flakes into what would eventually become planetary cores

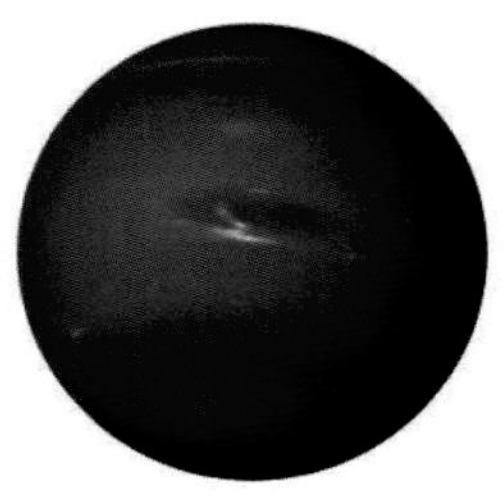

Gas giant Neptune was formed ***beyond*** the frost line; it is rich in ices, and its low temperature and high gravitational field strength have allowed Neptune to retain a deep atmosphere of hydrogen and helium.

Image credits: NASA

Beyond the frost line, the cores of the protoplanets grew to much bigger sizes than those of the terrestrial planets due to the large abundance of ices. The gravitational attraction by these massive cores was able to draw in copious amounts of hydrogen and helium gas that was present in the outer Solar System to form the substantial atmospheres of the four gas giant planets.

It is probable that internal radioactive heating then caused cores to melt and less dense materials to rise upwards. This created semi-molten mantles and solid crusts for the terrestrial planets and slushy mantles for the gas giants.

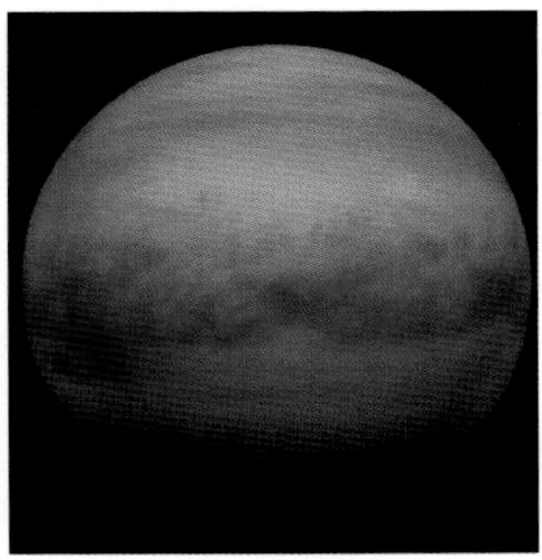

Clouds in the dense atmosphere of Venus: despite its high temperature, Venus is massive enough to retain an atmosphere.

Some planets retained a significant amount of gas in their atmospheres. The presence of an atmosphere is determined by two opposing factors:

- A planet or moon's mass: the greater the mass, the greater the gravitational pull on the atmosphere;
- Temperature: the hotter the temperature, the faster the gas molecules move, making them more likely to 'escape' the gravitational attraction of the planet or moon.

Saturn's large moon Titan: a combination of large mass (gravitational attraction) and low temperature make Titan unique in the Solar System as the only moon to have a significant (nitrogen-rich) atmosphere (shown in blue).

Image credits: NASA

Planetary scientists suggest that the early Solar System was a chaotic world containing over 50 bodies that collided, broke apart and re-formed a significant number of times before becoming an ordered system of 8 planets in stable orbits under the influence of the Sun's gravitational attraction.

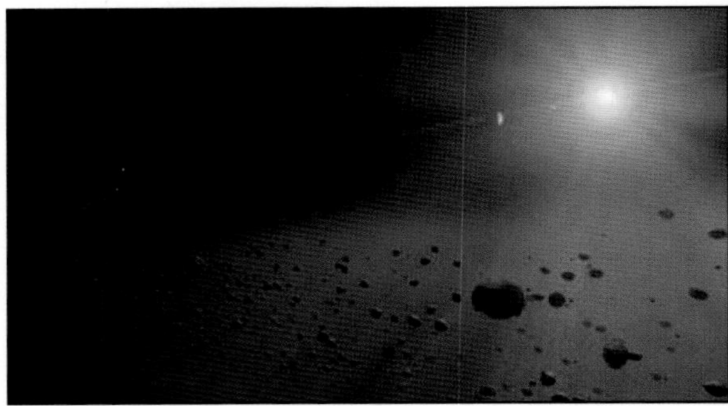

Right: An artist's impression (*courtesy of physicsworld.com*) of the Solar System in its early formative stages.

To support this suggestion, there is substantial evidence for collisions on a variety of scales during the Solar System's history:

- Mercury's iron core occupies over 60% of its volume (compared with < 20% for the Earth); the planet is thought to have lost most of its rocky interior due to a collision with a protoplanet about one sixth of its size;
- Changes in axial tilts: the 'backwards' spin of planet Venus and 'sideways' spin of Uranus suggest that these two planets suffered significant blows during the Solar System's history;
- Numerous impact craters on planets, asteroids and moons.

The Planets: the definitive visual guide is a superb illustrated account of what is currently known about the planets, moons and smaller bodies that make up our Solar System.

Look out for this at discount retail outlets such as *The Works*.

It is also possible that the orbits of some planets and moons have been modified by large collisions at some time or other.

The surface of Phobos, the larger of Mars' two moons, contains unusual straight, parallel grooves. It is possible that these were 'carved' by ejecta from Mars following a meteoroid collision.

Image credit: NASA

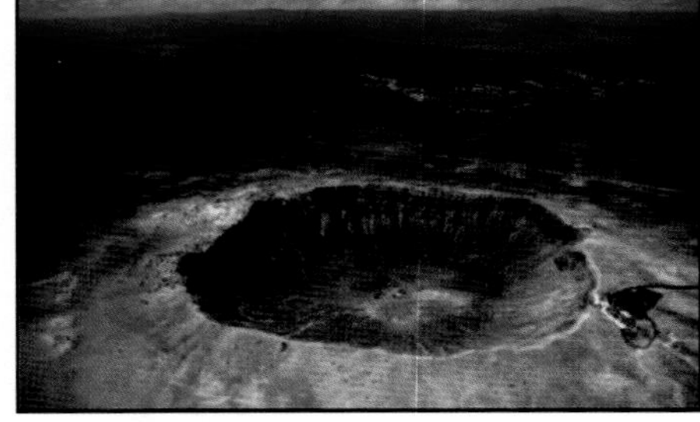

Meteor Crater (also known as **The Barringer Crater**) in Arizona, is one of the few surviving large impact craters on Earth; the majority have been eroded by water or the wind.

Image credit: Sol Santa Cruz

Although the planets are spherical, the shape of moons and asteroids depends on their size. An icy moon with a diameter less than about 400 km is unable to pull itself into a sphere because its mass is not great enough to generate sufficiently strong gravitational force to overcome the body's (elastic) resistance to it being deformed. For a rocky moon, that has stronger resistive forces, the size is slightly larger (about 600 km).

Gravitational attraction is also responsible for many of the moons of the planets, especially the outer moons of the gas giants. Whereas most of the larger moons (such as the four Galilean moons of Jupiter) were formed *in situ* with their host planet - they all orbit in the same plane and spin in the same sense - many other moons were 'captured' from the Asteroid or Kuiper Belts and have a range of orbit inclinations and spins.

Saturn's icy moon Mimas: at just under 400 km in diameter, Mimas is the smallest astronomical body to be spherical in shape.

Image credit: NASA/JPL

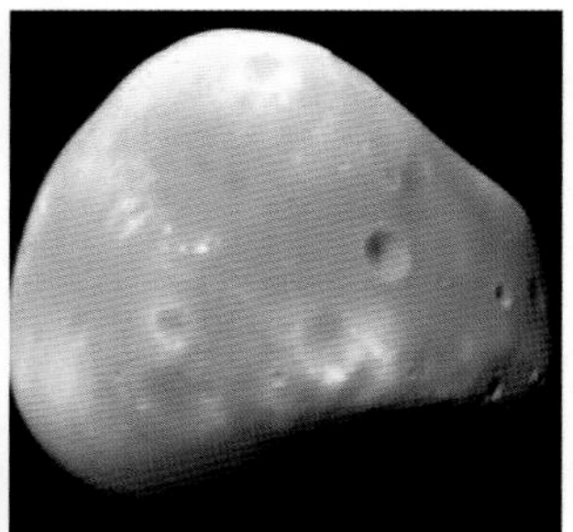

Deimos, the smaller of Mars' moons, is likely to have been captured from the Asteroid Belt.

Image credit: NASA

Saturn's moon Phoebe is probably a captured centaur (half-comet, half-asteroid).

Image credit: NASA

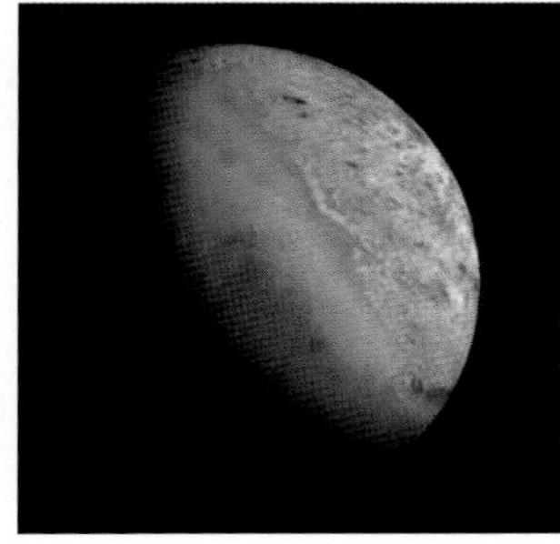

Scientists agree that Neptune's very unusual moon Triton is a captured KBO

Image credit: NASA

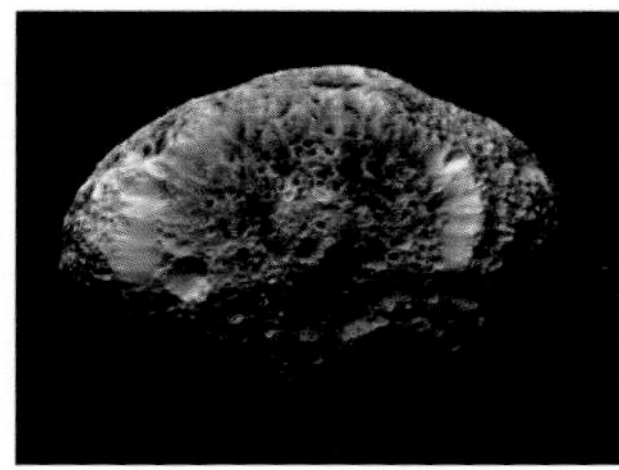

In contrast, Saturn's moon Hyperion is not quite large enough for gravitational forces to pull it into a sphere; its odd shape and sponge-like surface suggest that Hyperion is a fragment of a larger moon that was broken apart in a collision.

Image credit: NASA/JPL

Neptune's moon Triton is particularly odd. This has a circular, highly inclined, unstable orbit that is taking it closer and closer to Neptune; it will ultimately be broken up due to tidal forces (see below). Triton also shows evidence of cryovolcanism (see opposite), ejecting nitrogen gas and dark dust from its active geysers.

On page 36 of this book, we introduced the concept of **tidal forces** as being a consequence of the inverse square nature of gravitation. Let us explore these further.

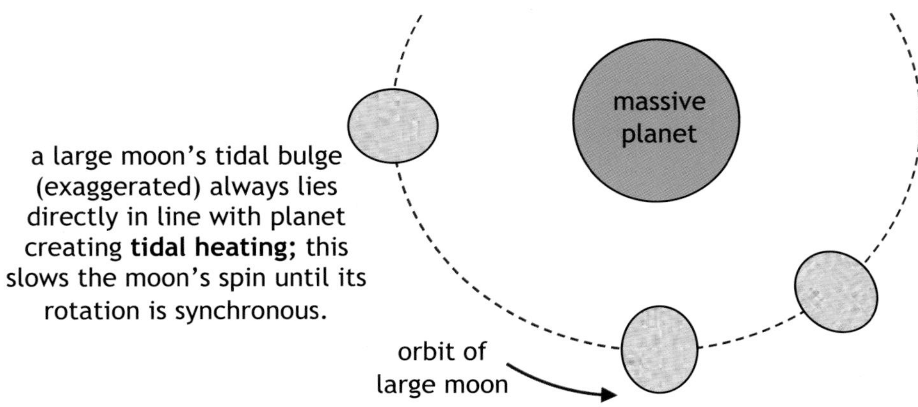

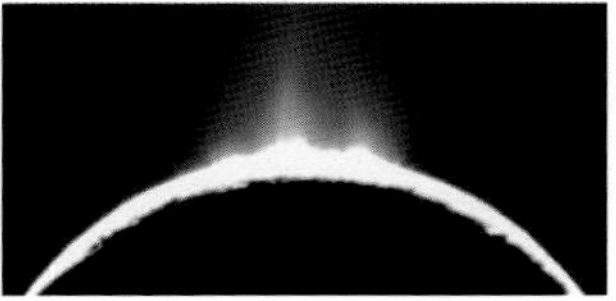

Evidence of ***cryovolcanism*** on Saturn's moon Enceladus: a cryovolcano ('ice volcano') is one that erupts volatiles such as water, ammonia and methane as opposed to molten rock.

Image credit: NASA

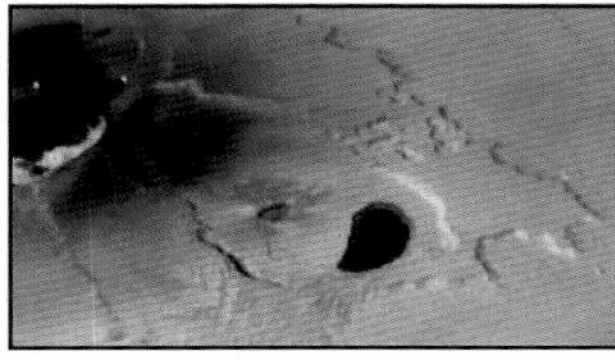

A close-up of Io shows many active volcanoes that continue to erupt from under its surface.

Image credit: NASA

Tidal forces can physically distort a large moon as it orbits a massive planet. The tidal bulges on an orbiting moon must lie directly in line with the planet and so as the moon spins, the tidal bulge must migrate around its surface.

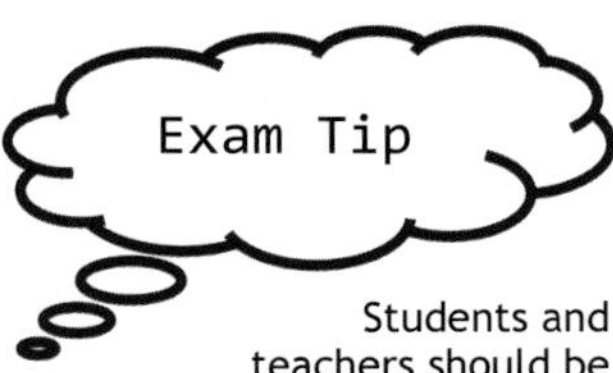

Students and teachers should be cautious when referring to 'heat' (which is a transfer of energy brought about by a temperature difference).

Avoid phrases such as '*internal friction generates heat*', because it doesn't: it produces ***thermal energy*** and hence a heating ***effect***.

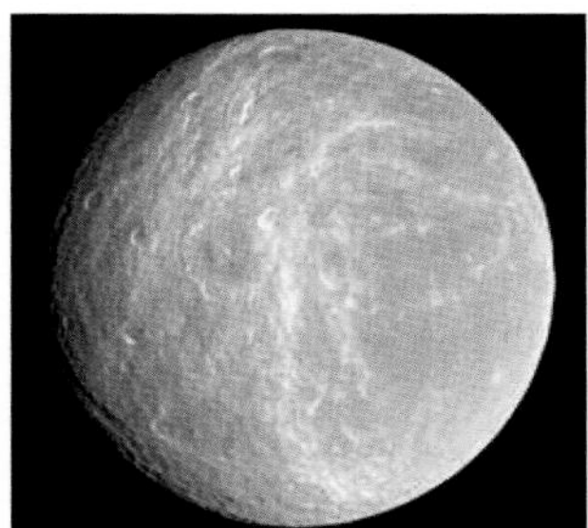

For some moons (for example Rhea), tidal forces may not be significant. This is either because the difference in the gravitational attraction on opposite sides of the moon may be too small (because of its small size) or because the moon is too far away from its parent planet to be affected significantly.

A giant planet has a diameter of 24 000 km.

What is the approximate value of the planet's Roche Limit?

Answer after Index

An impressive false-colour image of Saturn's complex rings consisting of billions of tiny fragments of ice.

It is possible that they were formed from the break-up of a small icy moon that was torn apart by Saturn's tidal forces.

Image credit: NASA

This causes a kind of 'internal friction' and the interior of the moon becomes warm; this is known as **tidal heating.** Thermal energy is produced at the expense of rotational kinetic energy, and the moon's spin slows down a little. Over time, this results in **synchronous rotation** in which the rotational and orbital periods are the same (as in the case of our Moon and most of the large moons of the massive gas giants).

 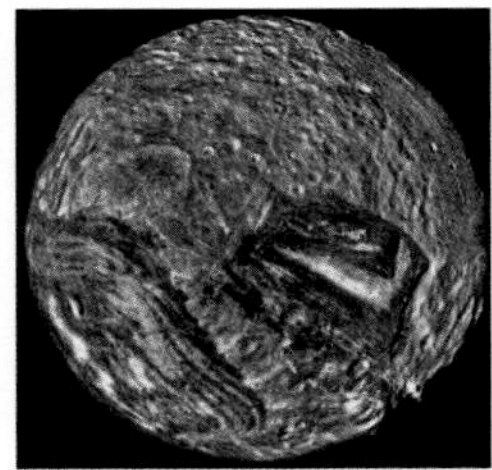 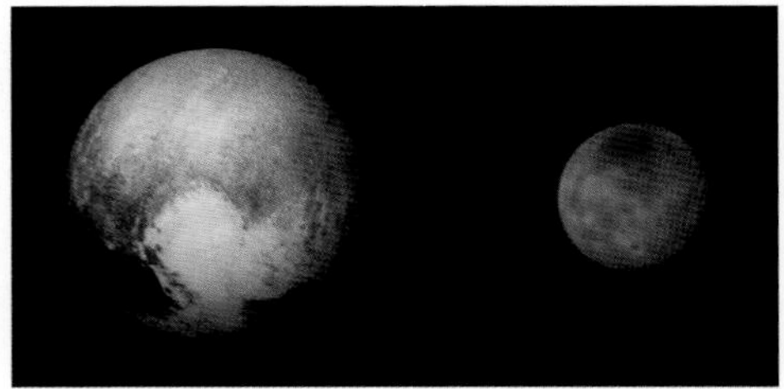

Tidal heating has resulted in synchronous rotation for many moons in the Solar System, including our own, the icy moon Miranda and Pluto's largest moon Charon.

Image credits: NASA

It is sensible to think that once synchronous rotation has been achieved, tidal heating ceases. This, however, is not the case because most orbits are elliptical and not circular: a moon's varying orbital speed means that tidal bulges still occur and 'oscillate' about a mean position.

In addition, the orbits of some moons are modified in multi-body interactions. For example, the orbital periods of Jupiter's moons Ganymede, Europa and Io are in the exact ratio of 4 : 2 : 1; this is known as **orbital resonance**. Regular gravitational tugs on Europa and Io mean that they do not orbit Jupiter in circular orbits and tidal heating continues.

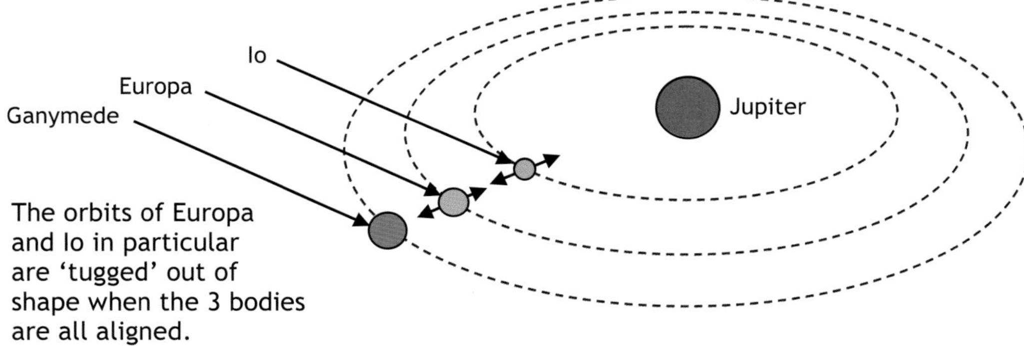

The orbits of Europa and Io in particular are 'tugged' out of shape when the 3 bodies are all aligned.

Tidal heating is also responsible for the molten layers that lie beneath the rocky or icy crusts of many of the large moons in the Solar System. These are responsible for the active volcanoes and ice volcanoes (cryovolcanoes) that are evident on their surfaces (see above).

A further consequence is that if a body's internal elastic forces that resist deformation are not strong enough, the dominant tidal forces will break up the body or prevent it from forming in the first place.

The minimum distance to which a large satellite can approach its parent body without being torn apart by tidal forces is known as the parent body's **Roche Limit.** For bodies of similar composition, its value is about 2.5 times the radius of the parent body.

This is a likely explanation of ring systems present around all the giant planets.

Finally in this section, we look at a situation in which the gravitational forces of two bodies create 'interesting' points in an orbit. These are the so-called **Lagrangian Points** in a two-body system (in this case, the Sun and the Earth) at which their combined force of gravity is equal to the centripetal force needed to maintain the circular motion of a third body such as a satellite.

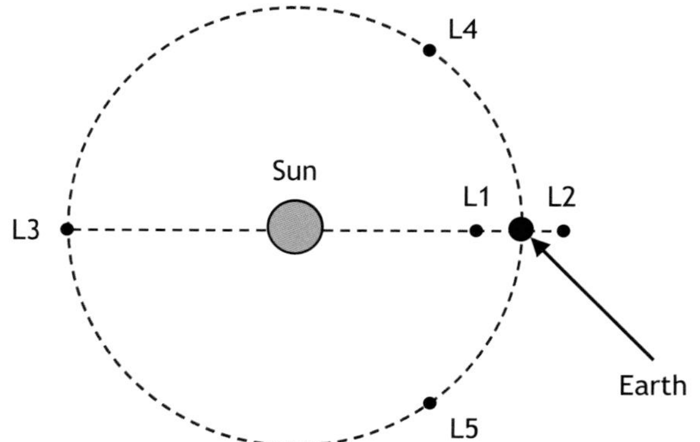

Lagrangian Points L1 - L5 are those at which the combined gravitational force due to two relatively massive bodies (such as the Sun and Earth) is equal to the centripetal force needed for an orbit.

Stable Lagrangian Points L4 and L5 are 60° ahead of, and behind, the Earth.

Of the 5 Lagrangian Points in the Sun - Earth system, points L1 - L3 are unstable, and a satellite located at any of these points needs continuous manoeuvring in order to maintain its orbit.

However, points L4 and L5 are stable and it is interesting to note that in the Sun - Jupiter two-body system, several asteroids (Trojans) are located at such points, leading and trailing Jupiter in its orbit by 60°; similarly, Dione and Tethys (two moons of Saturn) both have 'companion' moons 60° ahead and behind their respective orbital positions.

12.2 Exoplanets

The first system of **exoplanets** orbiting a star other than the Sun was discovered by Michel Mayor and Didier Queloz of the Observatoire de Genève in 1995. Since then, many more systems have been discovered using three indirect techniques that use observations of the stars:

- Astrometry (left): as massive exoplanets orbit their parent star, their combined gravitational pull can cause the star to move, or 'wobble' slightly in its position about the common centre of gravity (**G**); by precisely measuring the positions of a star, these small 'wobbles' can be detected;

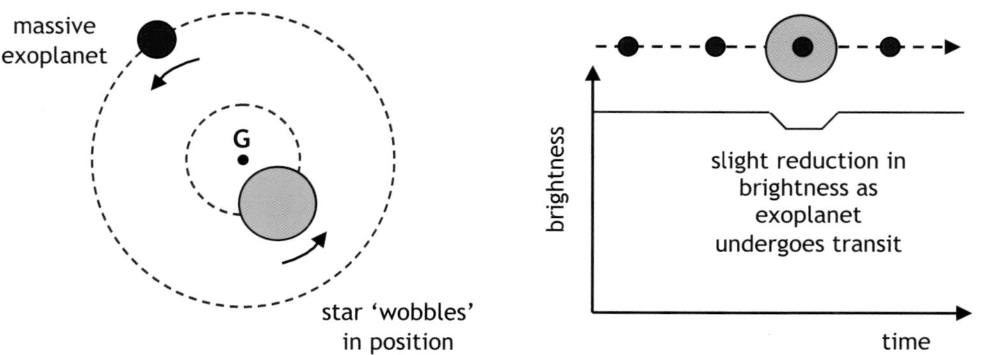

- Transit method (right): if exoplanets move across the disc of their host star during their orbit, they cause a very small (1%) drop in brightness for the duration of their transit; by monitoring the amount of light received from stars over long periods of time, these small 'winks' can be revealed;

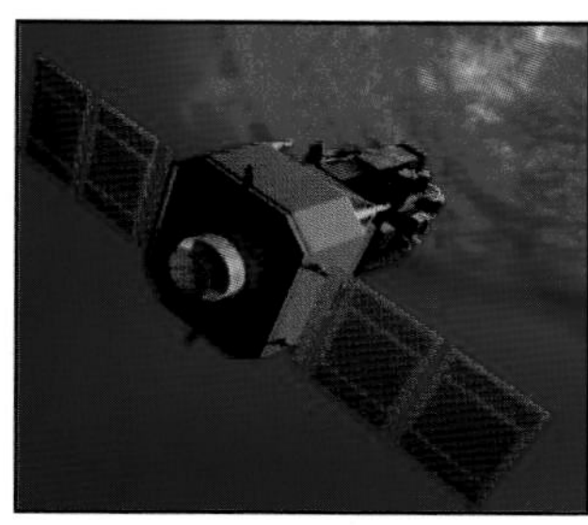

An artist's impression of the joint NASA/ESA *Solar and Heliospheric Observatory* (SOHO). The spacecraft is located close to L1, about 1.5 million km from Earth. Since this is located directly between the Earth and Sun, it allows continuous observation and measurements of the Sun, the corona, the solar wind and other solar phenomena.

Image credit: NASA

Exam Tip

Students need only be aware of the ***significance*** of Lagrangian Points: no mathematical descriptions are required.

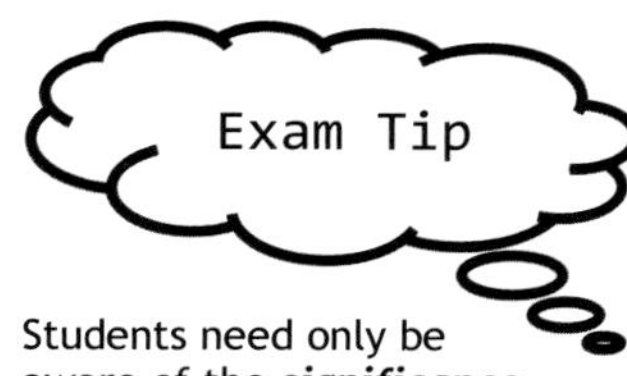

An artist's impression of Kepler-186f. This was the first rocky planet to be discovered within a star's **Habitable Zone** in which the temperature is just right to maintain liquid water on its surface.

Image credit: NASA Ames/SETI Institute/JPL - Caltech

An artist's impression of NASA's *Kepler* Space Telescope that has helped to discover hundreds of exoplanets orbiting other stars.

For more information, visit:

https://www.nasa.gov/feature/jpl/20-intriguing-exoplanets

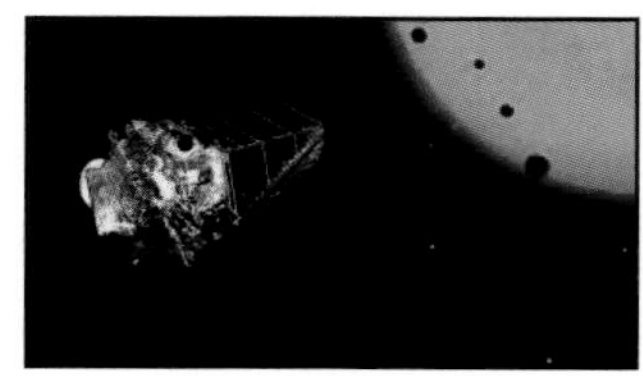

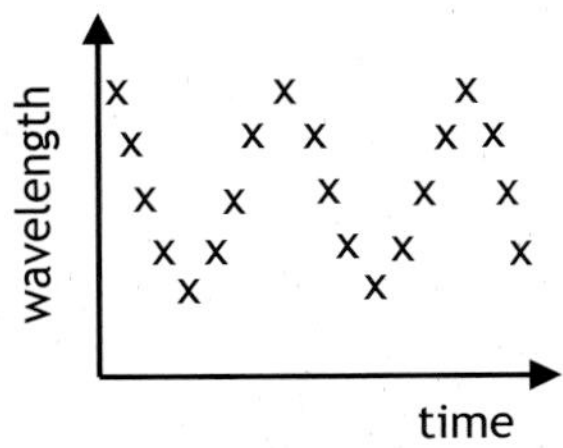

A graph of wavelength of a given spectral line against time; the regular to-and-fro movement of the star indicates the possible presence of exoplanets.

- Radial velocity method: the slight 'wobbling' of a star due to the orbital motion of an exoplanet can be detected as small Doppler-shifts (page 63) in the wavelengths of the star's spectral lines as it moves to and fro in the line-of-sight of the observer; astronomers use spectroscopy (page 54) to reveal these small changes, and it is this method that has proved the most successful to date at detecting exoplanets.

12.3 Extra-terrestrial life

In addition to a source of energy (e.g. from tidal or radioactive 'heating', or from a star), there are two essential chemical ingredients needed for life:

- Carbon: this element has the ability to make interesting compounds such as amino acids that form the building blocks of more complex organic molecules;
- Water: in its liquid state, this is an excellent solvent and acts as a transport mechanism for many nutrients.

A star's Habitable Zone is popularly known as its **Goldilocks Zone** because, like the porridge in the children's story, it is 'neither too hot nor too cold' for water to exist as a liquid.

Fortunately for us, our planet is located at just the right distance from the Sun for liquid water to exist; Earth is located within the Sun's Habitable (Goldilocks) Zone.

Image credit: popupbook.hk

Astronomers have identified at least three possible candidates that could support simple microscopic life within our Solar System:

An artist's impression of Saturn's largest moon Titan, with its seas of liquid hydrocarbons.

Image credit: NASA

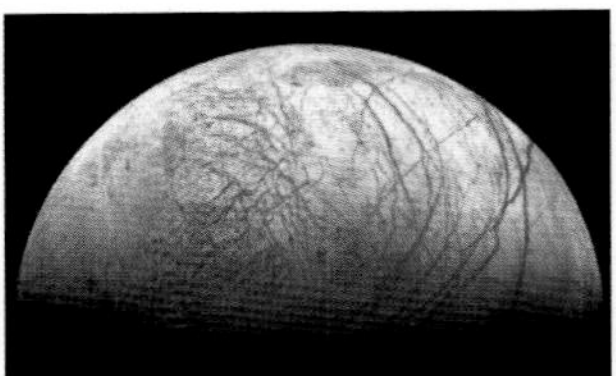

Jupiter's moon Europa contains an ocean of liquid water under its icy shell.

Image credit: NASA

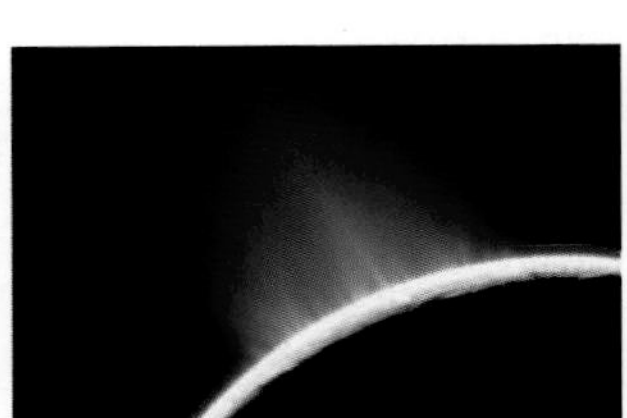

Plumes of salty water, ammonia, carbon dioxide and hydrocarbons erupt from Enceladus.

Image credit: NASA

Looking beyond our Solar System, a planet must be located within a star's **Habitable Zone** if liquid water is to exist on its surface. Since temperature decreases with distance from a star, the Habitable Zone corresponds to a relatively small range of distances from the star.

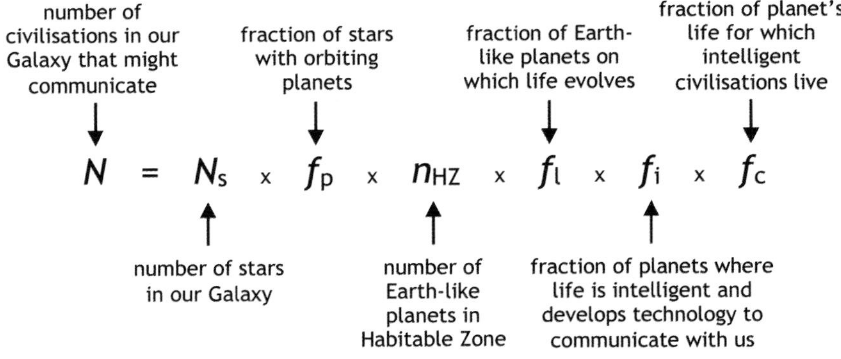

The SETI (Search for Extra-Terrestrial Life) Institute coordinates attempts that seek evidence of life in the Universe.

Find out more, or join them, at:

www.seti.org

There have been many attempts to estimate the likelihood of intelligent life that may exist elsewhere in our Galaxy. The **Drake Equation** (above) - there are slightly different forms of this - is the most well-known. It combines many numerical factors, such as the probability of a single star having a planetary system, to arrive at an approximate figure for the number of civilisations in our Galaxy that might have the technology to communicate with us.

13 Exploring starlight

13.1 Magnitudes

In ancient times, stars were placed in 6 **magnitude** classes in order to distinguish their observed brightness. Stars of first magnitude were the brightest since these very visible first after sunset. The next brightest stars were classified as second magnitude and so on, with the faintest visible stars having a magnitude of 6.

With modern optical instruments, we are able to distinguish small differences in brightness and so use decimal places to improve precision. In addition, the use of telescopes has required the magnitude scale to extend beyond 6, and magnitudes of zero and less are needed for very bright stars and some planets.

name of star	Bayer classification	apparent magnitude
Sirius	α CMa	-1.5
Rigel	β Ori	0.1
Polaris	α UMi	1.8
Ruchbah	δ Cas	2.7
	ζ Leo	3.4
	ψ Psc	5.5

brightest star in the sky → Sirius

no proper names for fainter stars → (ζ Leo, ψ Psc)

In a light-polluted sky, it is almost impossible to see stars of magnitude 3 or more; in dark-sky sites, magnitudes as faint as 6 can probably be seen.

A magnitude difference of 5.0 corresponds to a brightness ratio of 100. It follows that a magnitude difference of 1.0 corresponds to the fifth root of 100, which is 2.512.... For the purpose of GCSE (9-1) Astronomy, you will be pleased to know that 2.5 will suffice.

magnitude difference	ratio of brightness
1.0	2.5
2.0	2.5 x 2.5 = 6.25
3.0	16
4.0	40
5.0	100
6.0	250

So far we have been referring to the **apparent magnitudes** (***m***) of a star, i.e. how bright it ***appears*** in the night sky. This depends on four main factors:

- The total energy radiated by the star in the visible region;
- The distance to the star;
- The amount of interstellar gas and dust that reflects and absorbs light;
- The amount of light absorbed and scattered by the Earth's atmosphere.

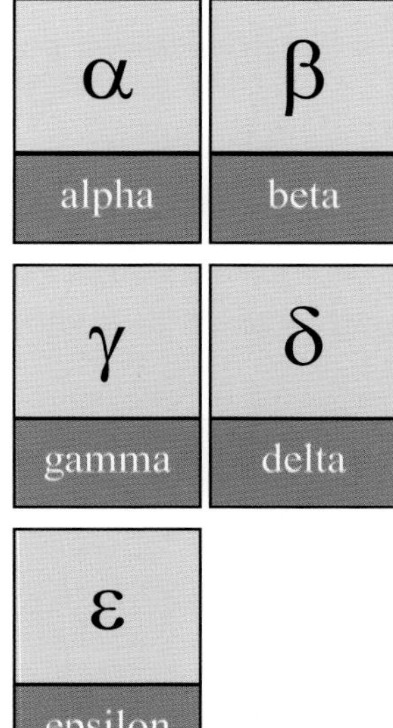

In 1603, the German astronomer Johann Bayer published his star catalogue *Uranometria* in which he used lowercase Greek letters to label the stars in each constellation in order of brightness (alpha for the brightest, beta for the second brightest and so on).

When labelling stars, the Greek letter is followed by the genitive (possessive) form of the constellation's Latin name, but this is often abbreviated.

For example, α Gem, β Per, γ Cas, δ UMi, and ε Ori.

Use the Bayer classification scheme to deduce the name of:

(a) the third brightest star in Cassiopeia

(b) the second brightest star in Cygnus

(c) the brightest star in Pisces

(d) the fourth brightest star in Hercules.

Answers after Index

Astronomers also use the term **absolute magnitude** (***M***) to refer to the true brightness of a star.

Absolute magnitude is defined at the star's apparent magnitude if the star was 10 parsec away from us. We will meet this unit of distance shortly, but in the meantime, the **distance modulus equation** relates the two magnitudes:

$$M = m + 5 - 5 \log d$$

where ***d*** is the distance to the star in parsecs. Further information on logarithms and how to perform calculations to find ***m*** or ***M*** can be found in the *Essential Maths Skills for GCSE (9-1) Astronomy* CD-ROM.

13.2 Spectroscopy and the H-R Diagram

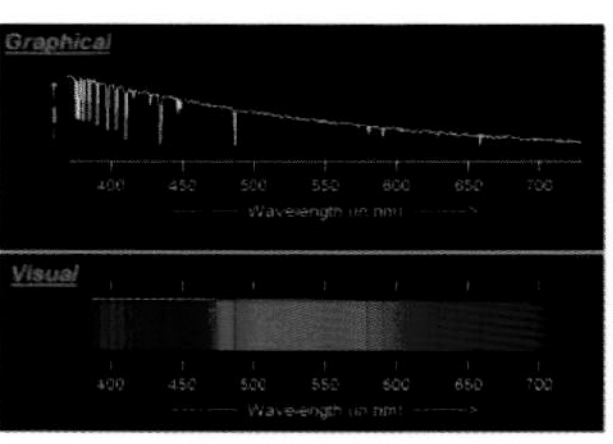

The spectra of stars can be studied either graphically or visually as a set of dark lines on a coloured background.

Image credit: University of Virginia

Despite what many people think, most professional astronomers do not look through telescopes or take photographs: they use the technique of **spectroscopy**. This involves collecting light with the aid of a large telescope and splitting up the light with a diffraction grating (in much the same way that Isaac Newton first did this using a glass prism) to obtain a **spectrum.**

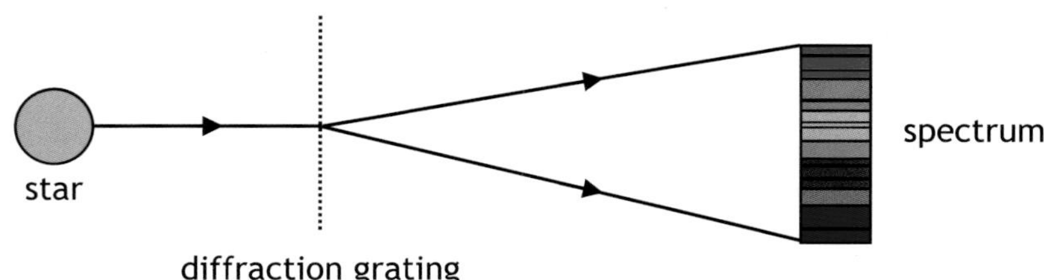

A compact disc and cardboard tube can be used to make a simple device to study spectra.

Visually, this is a set of dark lines on a continuous coloured background. The spectral lines correspond to the exact wavelengths at which atoms in the outer layers of stars absorb light; each chemical element has its own unique set of wavelengths and therefore 'fingerprint' set of spectral lines.

From studying the spectrum of a star, astronomers can identify which chemical elements are present, the temperature of the star and whether the star is moving towards or away from us in the line-of-sight: its radial velocity.

In addition, astronomers can examine the ratios of hydrogen : helium : other elements ('metals') to classify stars into different **spectral types**. The most common classification system uses a series of letters to define spectral types:

Arrange the following spectral types of stars in order of decreasing temperature:

G0 F1 B1

A6 K7

K4 G2

	O	B	A	F	G	K	M
mnemonic:	'Oh	Be	A	Fine	Girl / Guy	Kiss	Me'
temperature:	40 000 K ◄						2500 K
colour:	blue / white				yellow		red

Fine divisions are made by adding a number: A7, A8, A9, F0, F1, F2 etc.

It can be clearly seen from the graphic above that both a star's colour and spectral type are related to its surface temperature.

The H-R Diagram was formulated independently just over 100 years ago by Danish astronomer and chemist Ejnar Hertzsprung and American astronomer Henry Norris Russell. It has many different versions, but is essentially a scatter graph of either a star's luminosity or its absolute magnitude (***M***) against either spectral type or temperature (increasing to the left).

There are lots of video clips on YouTube that describe the H-R Diagram. We found one that first explains why different stars emit different colours of radiation:

https://www.youtube.com/watch?v=_EtlJCfaxdc

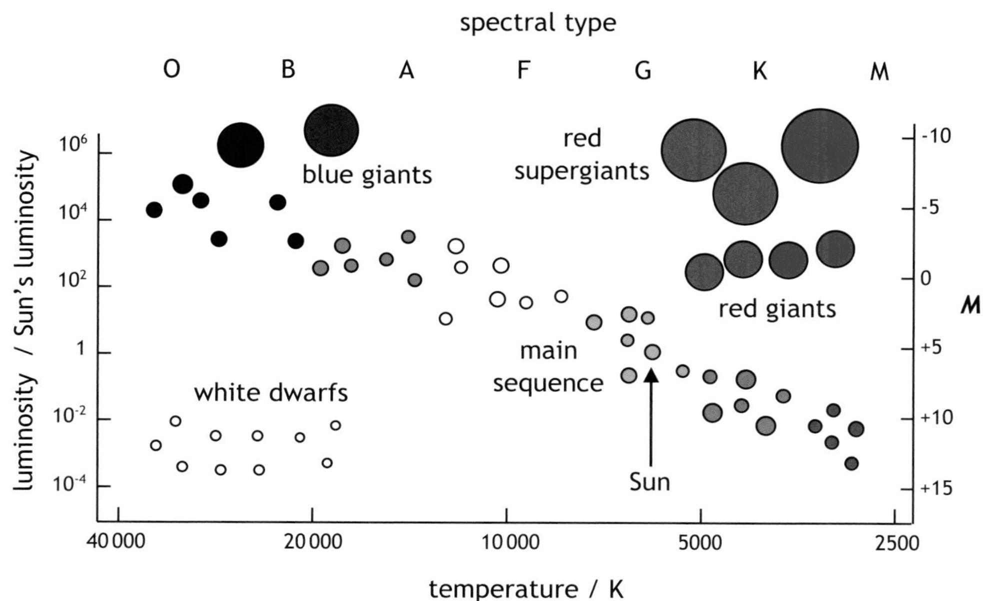

In Paper 2 of the written examination, students may be asked to sketch the H-R Diagram, labelling both axes and indicating the positions of the giants, supergiants and dwarfs.

Far from being randomly scattered, the properties of stars place them in 3 or 4 distinct groups:

- **Main sequence stars** lie in a band running from top left to bottom right; 90% of stars are main sequence stars; the Sun is a G2 main sequence star;
- **Giants** and **supergiant** stars lie above the main sequence; giants are red or blue in colour, but even-larger supergiants tend to be red;
- **White dwarf** stars lie below the main sequence towards the left.

We will explore how these groupings of star relate to stellar evolution later.

13.3 Stellar distances

On page 21, we introduced two units used by astronomers when they refer to distances outside the Solar System: light-years (l.y.) and parsecs (pc).

$$1 \text{ l.y.} = 9.5 \times 10^{12} \text{ km} \qquad 1 \text{ pc} = 3.1 \times 10^{13} \text{ km}$$

Light years tend to be used in 'popular astronomy' such as in magazines and by *Sky at Night* presenters, whereas professional astronomers favour the parsec (defined below). Like the similarity between the metre and the foot that we mentioned earlier, the light-year and the parsec have similar values, and in fact:

$$1 \text{ pc} = 3.26 \text{ l.y.}$$

One useful aspect of the H-R Diagram is that once a main sequence star's spectral type is known, its absolute magnitude can be 'read off' from the diagram. Thus can then be substituted along with its apparent magnitude into the distance modulus formula to calculate ***d***.

Blue is hot,
Red is cool.

The colour of a star is related to its surface temperature, but not in the way that many people think.

We normally associate the colour red with high temperature, but in fact the opposite is true for stars.

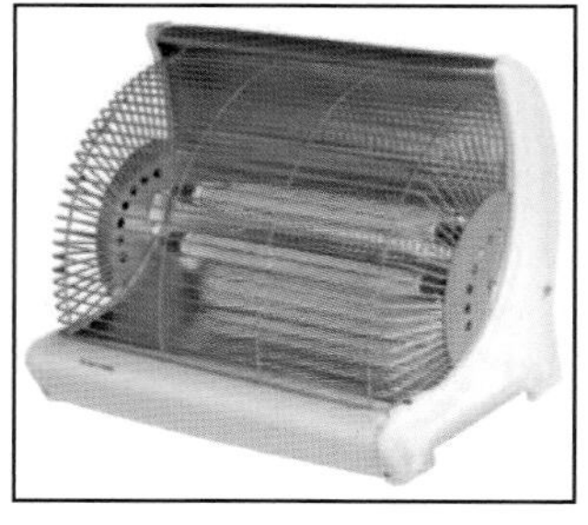

The filament of this electric heater is orange/red, and in everyday terms it is indeed hot.

However, assuming a hypothetical filament that does not melt, if the current was increased, the filament would glow yellow, white and then eventually blue.

The distances to relatively nearby stars can be determined using the technique of **heliocentric parallax.**

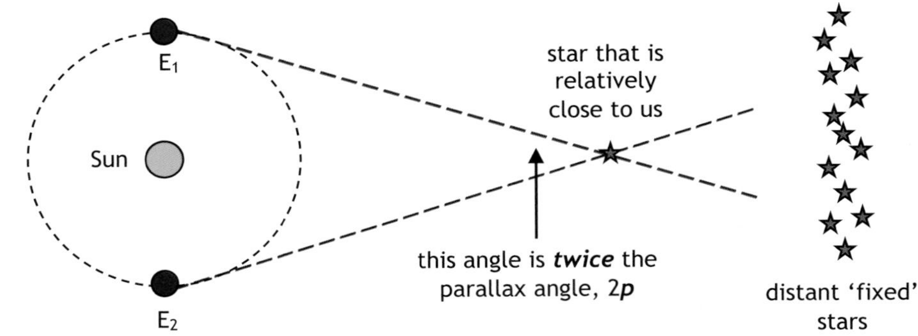

When we move our heads from side to side, nearby objects appear to move relative to more distant ones; this effect is known as **parallax.**

In a similar way, nearby stars appear to move in relation to distant stars when they are observed from different positions, in particular the two extremes of the Earth's orbit around the Sun (E_1 and E_2). ***Half*** of the small apparent shift in angular position is called the **parallax angle** of the star (***p***), and if its value is 1 arcsec, then by definition the distance (***d***) to the star is 1 pc.

It follows that:

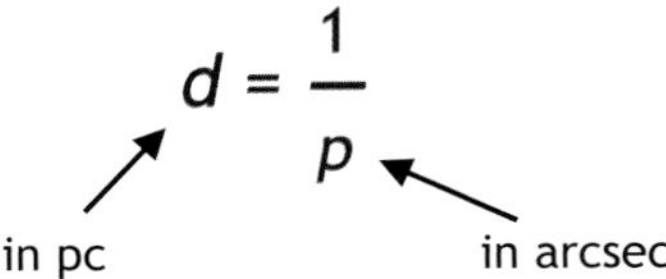

$$d = \frac{1}{p}$$

Minutes and seconds of arc

The degree is much too large an angle to be used in conjunction with parallax angles.

Astronomers split one degree into 60 minutes (of arc, as opposed to time):

1° = 60 arcmin (*abbr.*')

In addition, they split 1 arcmin into 60 seconds of arc, 60 arcsec (60'')

So there are 3600 arcsec in one degree, or

1 arcsec = 1/3600°

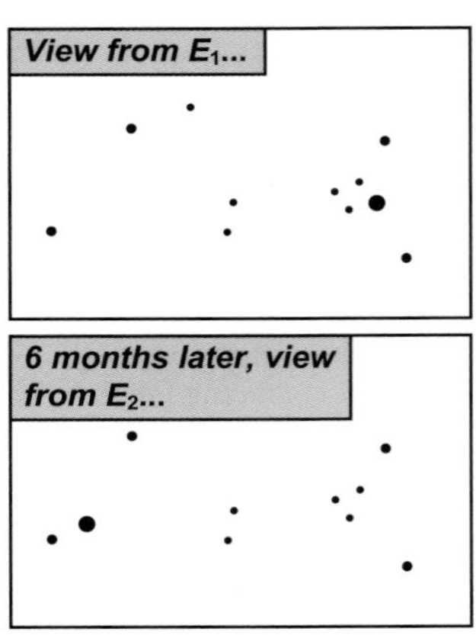

The (bright) nearby star appears to have moved its position in relation to the distant stars.

13.4 Variable stars

Although we would not notice during an observing session, the light detected from many stars varies regularly on a variety of timescales. There are many different types of these so-called **variable stars**: some of them vary in brightness due to some changing physical quantity such as size - they physically pulsate - whereas others vary due to changes in the amount of light reaching Earth (such as an eclipsing binary star).

Light curves (graphs of apparent magnitude against time) for some of the more common types of variable star (often named after their prototype) are shown below. We invite you to draw smooth curves through the points.

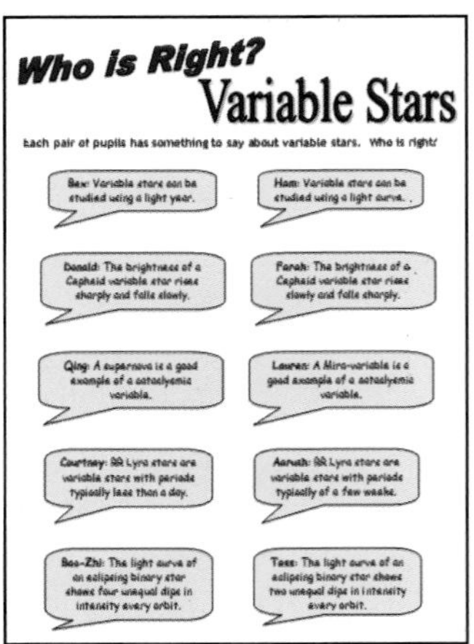

Who is Right?
Variable Stars

Each pair of pupils has something to say about variable stars. Who is right?

Bex: Variable stars can be studied using a light year.

Ham: Variable stars can be studied using a light curve.

Donald: The brightness of a Cepheid variable star rises sharply and falls slowly.

Farah: The brightness of a Cepheid variable star rises slowly and falls sharply.

Qing: A supernova is a good example of a cataclysmic variable.

Lauren: A Mira-variable is a good example of a cataclysmic variable.

Courtney: RR Lyra stars are variable stars with periods typically less than a day.

Aarush: RR Lyra stars are variable stars with periods typically of a few weeks.

Bao-Zhi: The light curve of an eclipsing binary star shows four unequal dips in intensity every orbit.

Tess: The light curve of an eclipsing binary star shows two unequal dips in intensity every orbit.

The 'Who Is Right?' worksheet on variable stars is just one of a large range of teaching resources contained in the *Lesson Starters & Plenaries* folder of our *New Teacher Toolbox for GCSE (9-1) Astronomy* CD-ROM.

The CD comes with an unlimited single-Centre site licence.

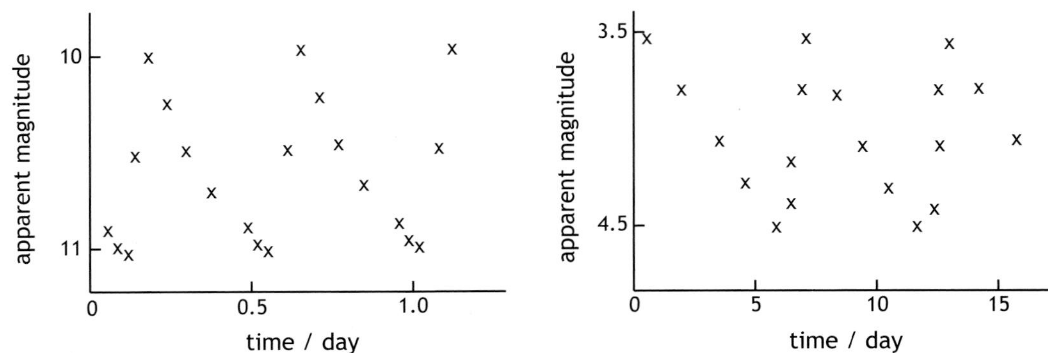

Typical light curve for a short-period RR Lyrae variable star

Light curve for a Cepheid variable star; the prototype is δ Cep

Cepheid variables are a class of giant yellow stars that expand and contract regularly. In 1912, American astronomer Henrietta Leavitt observed a number of these and established a relation between their period and average luminosity: a so-called **period - luminosity law**.

By determining the period of a Cepheid variable star, astronomers can deduce its absolute magnitude and use the distance modulus equation to calculate the distance to the star.

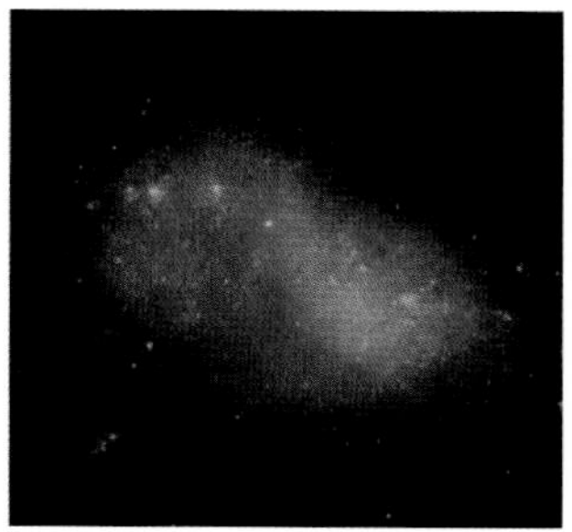

The Small Magellanic Cloud (SMC) is an irregular companion of the Milky Way Galaxy. In 1912, Henrietta Leavitt used observations of a number of Cepheid variables in the SMC to establish the period-luminosity law and hence a reliable way of determining stellar distances.

Image credit: NASA

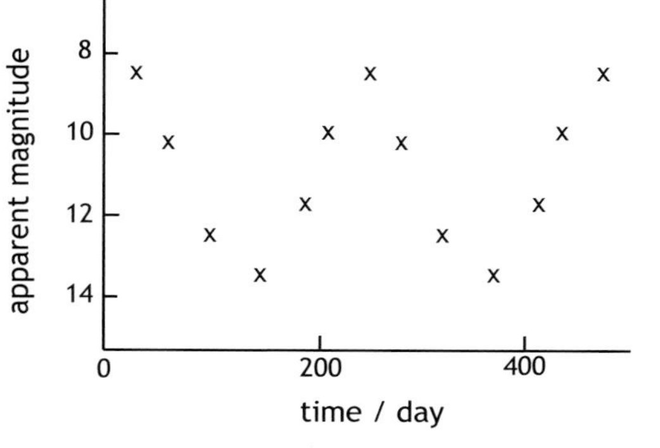

Typical light curve for a long-period (> 100 days) variable star e.g. Mira (ο Cet)

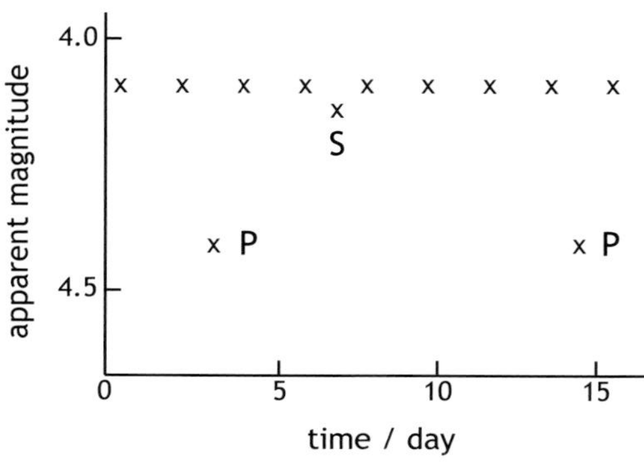

Light curve for an eclipsing binary star, e.g. Algol (β Per)

An **eclipsing binary** star consists of a bright primary star and dimmer secondary star in orbit around their mutual centre of gravity. When the secondary star eclipses (moves in front of) the primary, a large sharp drop in intensity is observed (P). When the primary star eclipses the dimmer secondary star, there is a smaller drop (S) in intensity.

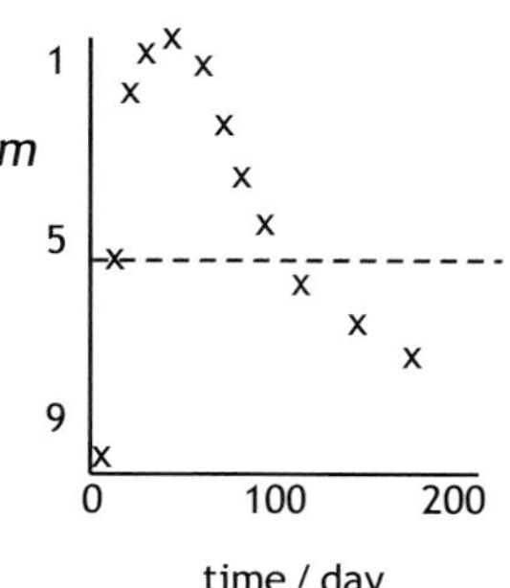

A supernova is classed as a type of ***cataclysmic variable*** in which an old, massive star blows itself apart (see chapter 14).

Points above the horizontal dashed line are visible with the naked eye.

13.5 Observing in other wavelength regions

There are many important branches of Astronomy in which scientists 'observe' in other (than visible) regions of the electromagnetic spectrum. Unfortunately, most of this radiation does not penetrate the Earth's atmosphere as far as ground level.

The diagram below shows the effect of our atmosphere on radiation in different wavebands of the electromagnetic spectrum (wavelength increases to the right): the lower the inverted 'bar', the more penetrating the radiation.

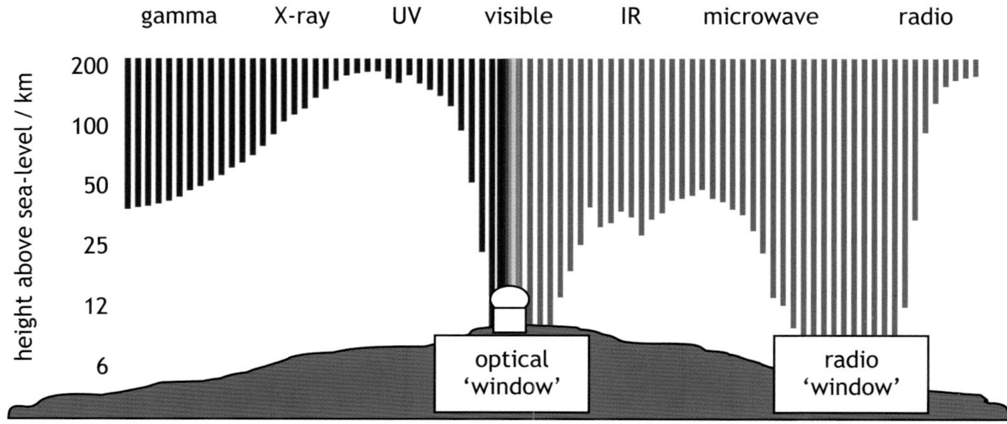

There are two main 'windows' in the atmosphere that allow radiation to pass through relatively unscathed: those for visible light and radio waves.

With its 76-m diameter reflecting 'dish', the Lovell Telescope at the Jodrell Bank Centre for Astrophysics is a striking landmark on the Cheshire Plain.

Only radio telescopes like this one, and optical telescopes, can be used for astronomical observations close to sea-level.

Image by the author

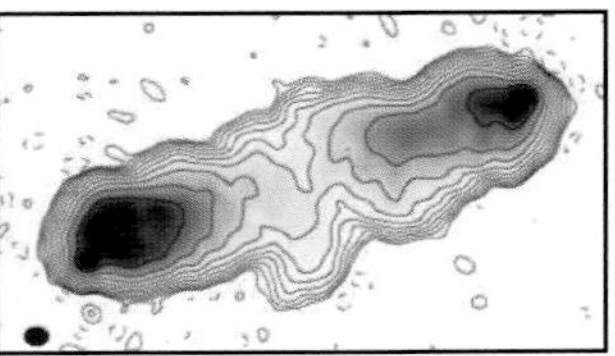

A contour map of the radio galaxy Cygnus A.

Image credit: Radboud University Department of Astrophysics

Most radio telescopes consist of a large concave 'dish' that reflects radio waves to a focus. Here, an aerial converts the radio waves into electrical signals that can be stored and processed (often as a contour map of the radio source).

Radio telescopes are large in order to achieve the best possible resolution of astronomical sources of radio waves (you may recall that the resolution of a telescope depends on the ***inverse*** of wavelength and that radio waves have much longer wavelengths than those of visible light).

Often, multiple radio telescopes at different sites are linked electronically to study the same source of radio waves. This technique is known as **aperture synthesis** and it effectively converts the array of telescopes into one large telescope with an aperture equivalent to the largest distance between individual telescopes.

An artist's impression of the Square Kilometre Array (SKA) of radio telescopes that will operate as an aperture synthesis system.

Image credit: The Cavendish Laboratory, University of Cambridge

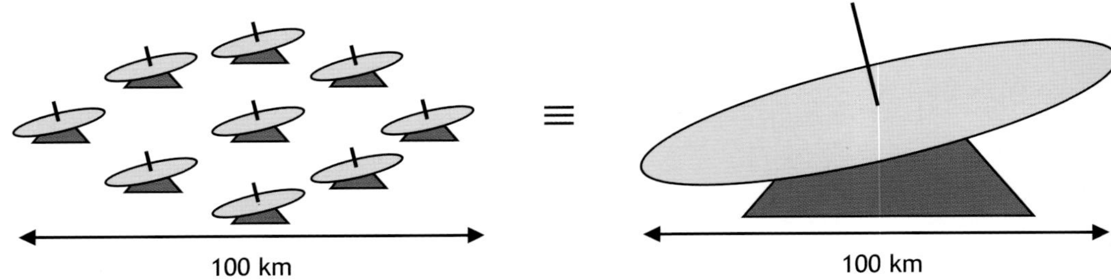

Although, like radio telescopes, optical telescopes can be sited at sea-level, most observatories are located on high mountains such as those in Hawaii, The Andes and The Canary Islands where the air is dry, steady and transparent.

Of course, the optimum location of a telescope is on a satellite orbiting above the Earth's atmosphere where there is no air to blur and absorb light, no day-night cycle and no light pollution from skyglow. Space telescopes do, however, have limited lifetimes and are very expensive to construct, launch and maintain.

What is meant by the 'baseline' of a radio telescope array?

Answer after Index

The table lists some of the key discoveries made by astronomers in different wavebands of the electromagnetic spectrum.

waveband	key discoveries
radio	quasars; structure and rotation of our galaxy; pulsars; protoplanetary discs; jets from black holes; SETI
infrared (IR)	protostars; interstellar dust and molecular clouds; 'hotspots' on moons
ultraviolet (UV)	corona and chromosphere structures of young stars
X-ray	active galaxies; accretion discs surrounding black holes; supernova remnants
gamma ray	gamma ray bursts in distant galaxies

The James Webb Space Telescope is scheduled for launch in late 2018 (at the time of writing). This infrared telescope will take over from NASA's highly-successful *Hubble Space Telescope* and be located at the Earth's L2 Lagrangian Point where it will shielded from the Earth's 'thermal noise'.

Image credit: NASA

In order to observe at wavelengths other than optical and radio, most observatories need to be fixed on observing platforms orbiting the Earth.

Infrared observatories are the one small exception to this - they can be sited on high mountains along with optical observatories - but even so, observing from above the atmosphere brings many advantages that may justify the high costs.

14 Stellar evolution

14.1 Nebulae and clusters

If we know in which directions to look, a few 'faint and fuzzy' objects are visible in the night sky with the naked eye; these were once generally known as **nebulae** (*sing.* nebula). With the benefit of a pair of binoculars or a small telescope, their appearances allow us to divide nebulae into four main types:

- **Open clusters** of young stars, mostly within the spiral arms of our Galaxy (such as the Pleiades);
- Large interstellar clouds of gas and dust to which the term **nebula** now refers (such as the Orion Nebula);
- **Globular clusters** of old stars that surround the centre of our Galaxy;
- Distant **galaxies**, such as the Andromeda Galaxy and the Magellanic Clouds.

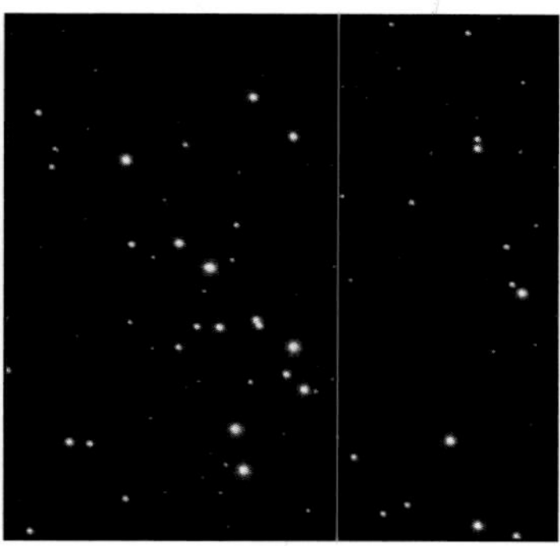

Left to right: The globular cluster M79 in the constellation of Lepus, the open cluster M48 in the constellation of Hydra and the emission nebula M43, close to the Orion Nebula. All the images were obtained by GCSE Astronomy student Claire Martin with the aid of the Faulkes 2-m robotic telescope located at Siding Springs in New South Wales, Australia. 'M' numbers refer to entries in the Messier Catalogue.

The Faulkes Telescope Project is just one of three robotic telescope facilities available without charge to schools (at the time of writing). The telescopes are ideal for observing extended objects such as nebulae and galaxies.

Find out more at:

www.faulkes-telescope.com

For the National Schools Observatory's Liverpool Telescope, visit:

www.schoolsobservatory.co.uk

For the Bradford Telescope, go to:

www.telescope.org

In 1781, the French astronomer Charles Messier published his revised *Catalogue of Nebulae and Star Clusters* that contained 103 extended astronomical objects (further entries have since been added and the number now stands at 110).

It is interesting to note that it was not Messier's intention to provide a catalogue for astronomers to observe, but rather to provide a list of objects to avoid: Messier was only interested in discovering comets!

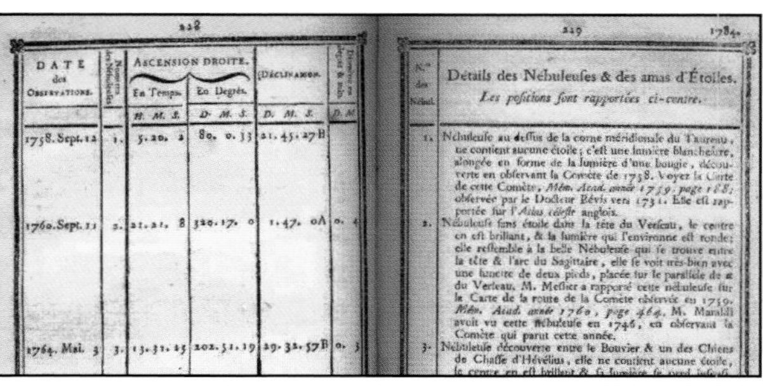

228

DATE des Observations.	Numéros des Nébuleuses	Ascension Droite. En Temps. H. M. S.	En Degrés. D. M. S.	Déclinaison. D. M. S.	Diamètre en degrés & min. D. M.
1758. Sept. 12	1.	5. 20. 2	80. 0. 33	21. 45. 27 B	
1760. Sept. 11	2.	21. 21. 8	320. 17. 0	1. 47. 0 A	0. 4
1764. Mai. 3	3.	13. 31. 25	202. 51. 19	29. 32. 57 B	0. 3

229 1784.

N.os des Nébul.	Détails des Nébuleuses & des amas d'Étoiles. *Les positions sont rapportées ci-contre.*
1.	Nébuleuse au dessus de la corne méridionale du Taureau, ne contient aucune étoile; c'est une lumière blanchâtre, alongée en forme de la lumière d'une bougie, découverte en observant la Comète de 1758. Voyez la Carte de cette Comète, *Mém. Acad. année 1759, page 188*; observée par le Docteur Bévis vers 1731. Elle est rapportée sur l'*Atlas céleste* anglois.
2.	Nébuleuse sans étoile dans la tête du Verseau, le centre en est brillant, & la lumière qui l'environne est ronde; elle ressemble à la belle Nébuleuse qui se trouve entre la tête & l'arc du Sagittaire, elle se voit très-bien avec une lunette de deux pieds, placée sur le parallèle de α du Verseau. M. Messier a rapporté cette nébuleuse sur la Carte de la route de la Comète observée en 1759. *Mém. Acad. année 1760, page 464.* M. Maraldi avoit vu cette nébuleuse en 1746, en observant la Comète qui parut cette année.
3.	Nébuleuse découverte entre le Bouvier & un des Chiens de Chasse d'Hévélius, elle ne contient aucune étoile, le centre en est brillant & sa lumière [illegible]

An extract from Messier's original catalogue shows the dates of observation and the celestial coordinates of his entries.

In the telescopes of Messier's day, distant nebulous objects could easily be mistaken for his preferred cometary targets.

Charles Messier earned the nickname of '*Furet des Cometes*' (Ferret of comets) from the French King Louis XV.

There are other catalogues of nebulae, clusters and galaxies: Patrick Moore's Caldwell Catalogue is an extension of Messier's, and the New General Catalogue (NGC), published by J. L. E. Dreyer in 1888, lists over 8000 extended objects (most of which are only visible with the aid of large telescopes).

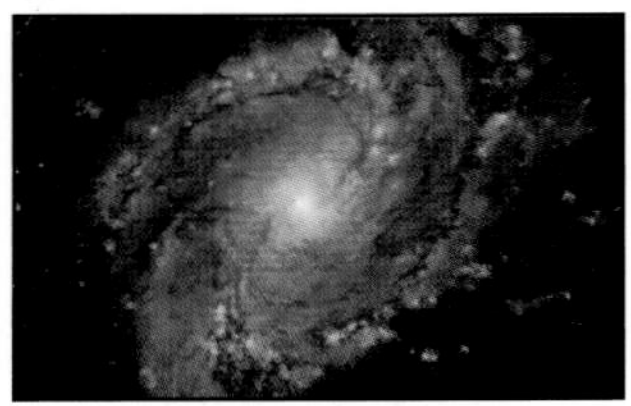

The Southern Pinwheel galaxy (M83) in the constellation of Hydra. The bright pink regions in the spiral arms are sites of current star formation.

Image credit: NASA

14.2 Evolution of low-mass stars (similar to the Sun)

All stars have their origin in the gravitational collapse of cool, dense **molecular clouds** of gas and dust that are found in the spiral arms of galaxies. As the cloud collapses, it is unstable and fragments into smaller clumps (**protostars**) that will eventually form the cores of individual stars.

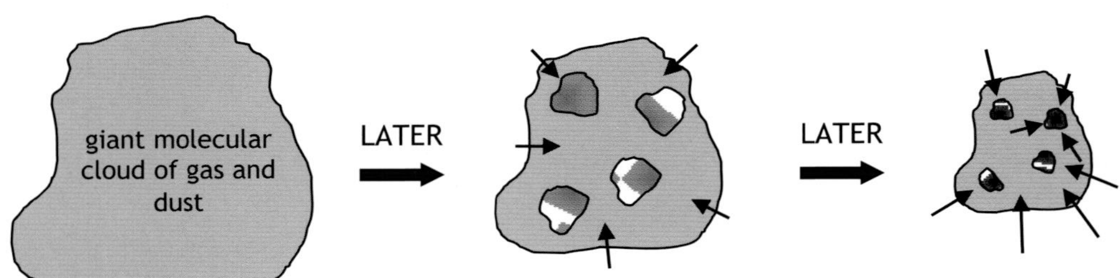

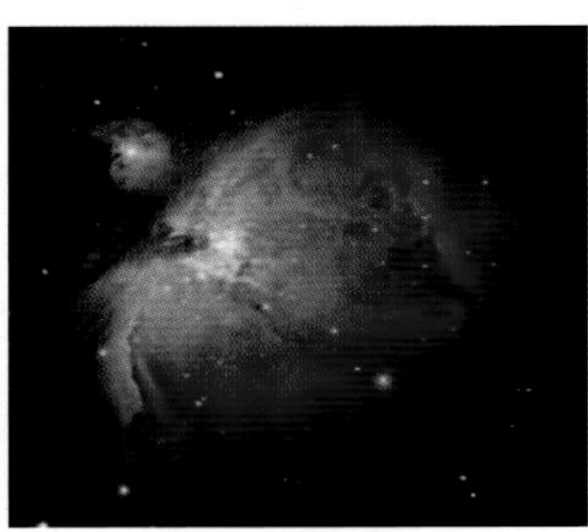

The Orion Nebula (M42) is both an **emission** and **absorption nebula**. The swirling cloud of hydrogen gas is illuminated by the UV radiation emitted by four hot, young stars embedded within the nebula. Eventually, several hundred stars will be born here.

Image credit: NASA

As each protostar collapses, gravitational potential energy is converted into kinetic energy and its temperature increases. Eventually this becomes hot enough for the nuclear fusion of hydrogen into helium (page 34) to occur; it is at this moment that the star is said to be 'born' onto the main sequence of the H-R Diagram.

The energy radiated by the core (the so-called **radiation pressure**) quickly balances and stops any further gravitational collapse of the star, and the star will continue for 90% of its lifetime as a main sequence star.

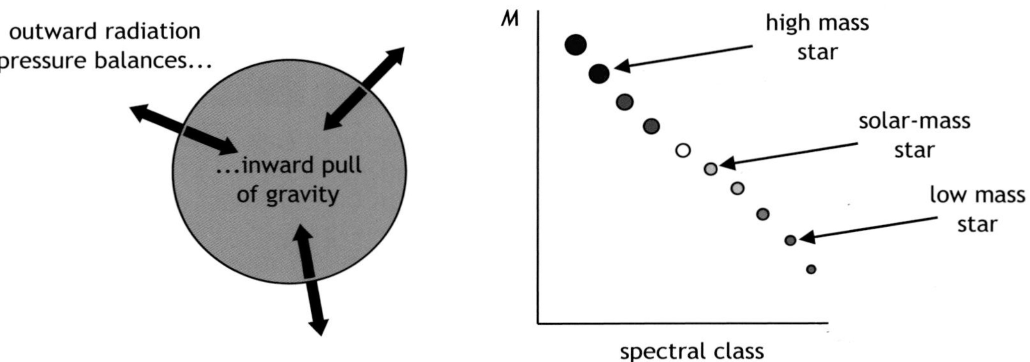

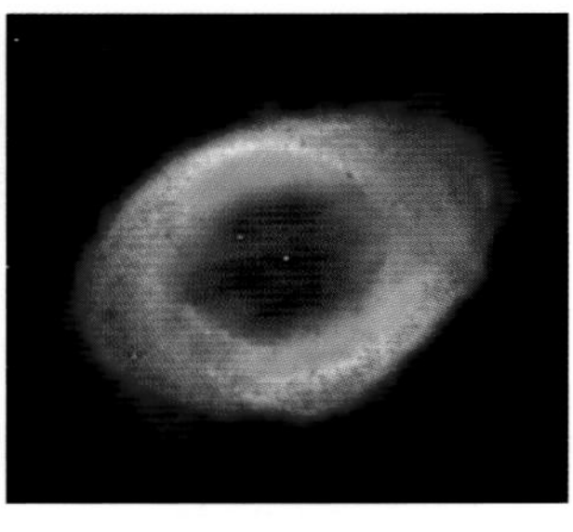

The Ring Nebula (M57) is a planetary nebula in the constellation of Lyra.

Image credit: NASA

Eventually, the amount of hydrogen able to fuse runs out. The subsequent evolution of a star depends on its mass, and we will consider separately:

- a low-mass star (with a core mass less than the so-called **Chandrasekhar Limit** of 1.4 times the mass of the Sun);
- a massive star.

In a low-mass star, the generation of energy stops, the radiation pressure becomes zero and gravitational collapse of the core occurs. This raises the temperature of the star and causes hydrogen to fuse once more but this time in a shell surrounding the core. The core of helium contracts further, rises in temperature, increases the rate at which energy is generated in the hydrogen shell and as a result, the star expands and cools to become a **red giant**. If the core temperature becomes hot enough, helium will fuse to form carbon.

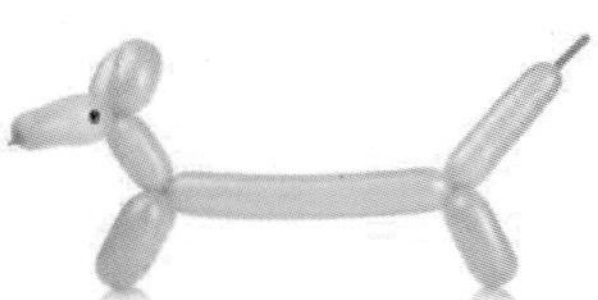

Just as a balloon often looks 'darker' at its rim (owing to observing through a deeper layer of rubber), a planetary nebula is more visible at its outer edges, giving a false 2-dimensional appearance.

The outer layers of the star continue to expand and are visible as an expanding sphere of gas called a **planetary nebula** (so-called because of the supposed resemblance to the telescopic appearance of some planets).

The core of the star eventually stops collapsing because of a new outward force called **electron (degeneracy) pressure**: in simple terms, the electrons cannot be squeezed together any closer and so resist further implosion. When this occurs, the star is still hot but very small: a **white dwarf**. Over time, this will continue to cool and ultimately become a **black dwarf**.

A white dwarf star (left) is similar in size to the Earth, but its mass is about half that of the Sun. It gradually cools from ~100 000 K until it eventually becomes an invisible black dwarf.

Image credit: Sky & Telescope

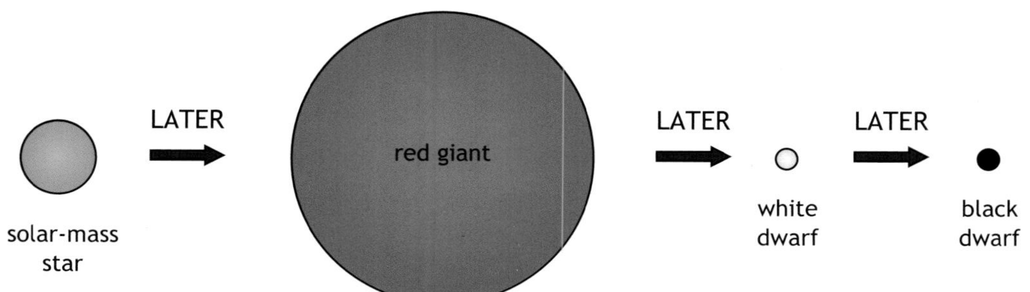

14.3 Evolution of massive stars

A star with core mass greater than the Chandrasekhar Limit continues to collapse and causes the temperature to be so high as to fuse carbon into neon. The subsequent cycle of fuel exhaustion - core collapse - new fusion reactions continues until the element iron is formed in the core.

During this time, the star will expand to be a red or blue **supergiant**.

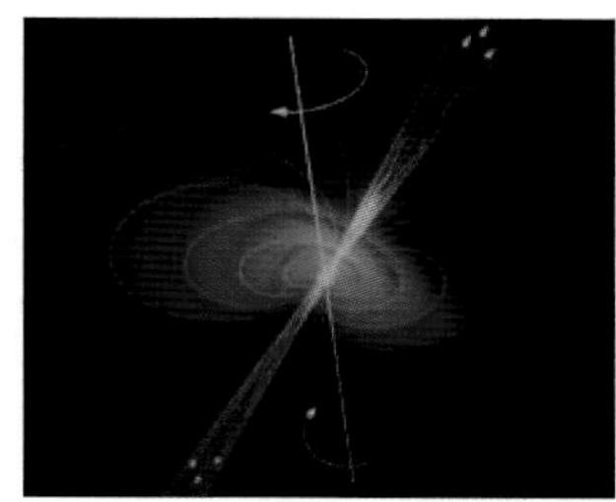

Model of a pulsar:
the neutron stars produced in supernovae rotate very rapidly and emit pulses of radio waves from polar hotspots.

Image credit: UCL

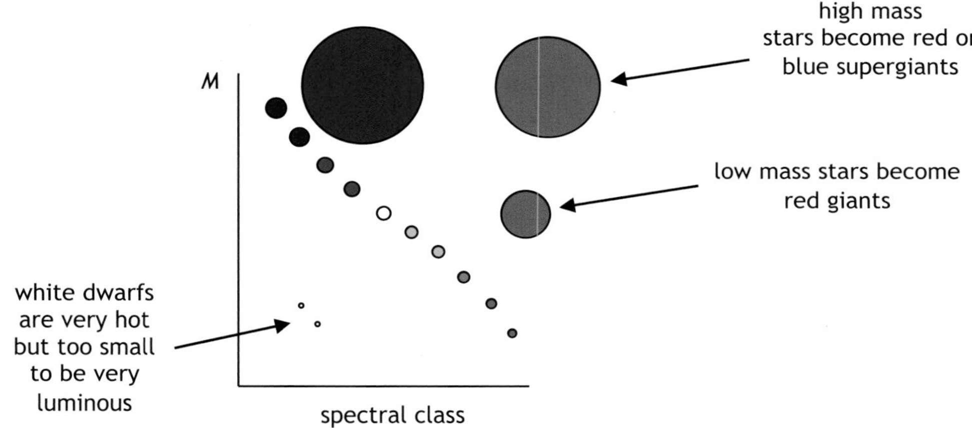

It is not possible to fuse iron into other elements and release energy. The massive star runs out of fuel and collapses under its own gravity but new nuclear reactions are unable to occur.

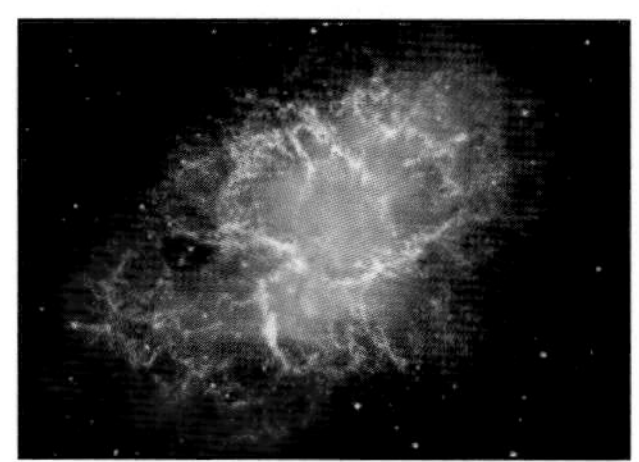

The Crab Nebula (M1) in the constellation of Taurus is the remnant of a supernova that was witnessed by Chinese astronomers in the year 1054.

Image credit: NASA

The mass of the star's core dictates the final stage. If the core's mass is no greater than about 3 times that of the Sun, its collapse is halted by **neutron (degeneracy) pressure**: in simple terms, the electrons have been forced into protons to form a solid core of neutrons, and these neutrons now resist being squeezed closer together.

The star has become a 20-km diameter **neutron star** and the sudden halt in core contraction causes a shock wave that blows the star apart in a **supernova** explosion, enriching the interstellar medium with chemical elements up to iron (that were created in the star) and new, heavier ones formed in the supernova.

An artist's impression of matter from a close neighbouring star falling onto a black hole. The accelerating matter generates X-rays, allowing the 'invisible' black hole to be detected.

Image credit: NASA

If the mass of the core is greater than about 3 solar masses, even neutron pressure is insufficient to halt the gravitational collapse following the supernova, and the core collapses further to become a **black hole**.

15 Our place in the Galaxy

15.1 The Milky Way

'The [Milky Way] *galaxy is, in fact, nothing but a collection of innumerable stars grouped together...'*

Galileo Galilei, astronomer

As Galileo informed us when he observed the Milky Way through his simple telescope, stars are not distributed uniformly throughout the Universe, but are grouped into huge gravitationally-bound collections called **galaxies** (with very little in between).

All the stars that are visible at night - plus about 200 billion more - reside in a galaxy called the Milky Way (Latin: *Via Lactea*); the name arises from its appearance as a faint patchy band of light stretching across the sky through constellations such as Cassiopeia, Perseus and Crux (the Southern Cross).

The Milky Way, observed from an observatory on Cerro Tololo high in The Andes.

This faint band stretching across the sky can be resolved into thousands of stars by binoculars or a small telescope.

Also visible (left) are two 'satellite' galaxies, the Small and Large Magellanic Clouds.

Image credit: Roger Smith/NOAO/AURA/NSF

When we observe the Milky Way in the night sky, we are looking into the plane of our Galaxy where most stars are located.

From a vantage point 'above' the plane of the Milky Way, it would resemble a giant disc-shaped Catherine Wheel rotating around a central bulge or nucleus, rather like the image of our closest galactic neighbour the Andromeda Galaxy (below left). There might also be a hint of a central bar running through the nucleus from which the spiral arms emerged.

From the 'side', our Galaxy resembles 'two back-to-back fried eggs':

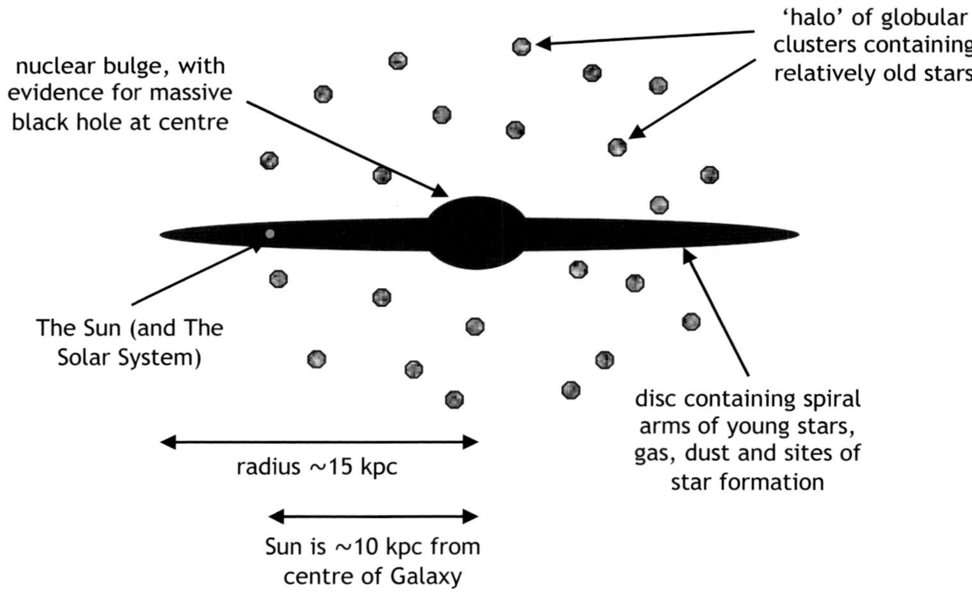

The Andromeda Galaxy, our closest galactic neighbour, is similar in shape and size to our Galaxy.

The central bulge and spiral arms are clearly visible, as are sites of current star formation.

Image credit: NOAO/AURA/NSF/ T.Rect & B.A.Wolpa

As we noted in the previous chapter, the spiral arms contain the gas and dust that are the sites of future star formation.

'We cannot see through to the centre of the Galaxy because there is too much dust in the way; it is rather like standing in Parliament Square and trying to read the dial of Big Ben on a foggy night.'

Sir Patrick Moore, astronomer

The barred spiral galaxy NGC 4603 in the constellation of Centaurus. Its bright spiral arms are clearly visible, as is the presence of intricate dust lanes.

The two bright 'spiky' stars are those in our Galaxy that happen to be in the same line-of-sight as NGC 4603.

Image credit: NASA

The spiral arms of our Galaxy do not allow visible light to penetrate because of dust, and so astronomers are unable to 'see' their structure and motion.

Fortunately, the spiral arms contain hydrogen atoms that reveal themselves by emitting radio waves. These are produced when single electrons orbiting hydrogen nuclei reverse their spin; the small loss in energy is radiated as electromagnetic radiation corresponding to a wavelength of 21 cm.

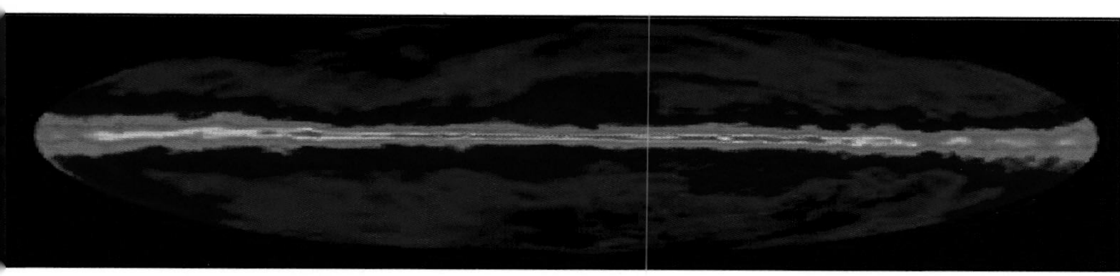

A panoramic 21-cm radio map of our Galaxy: the highest intensity of radio emission is shown in red.

Image credit: NASA

As our Galaxy rotates, the received 21-cm radio waves are Doppler-shifted to slightly shorter and longer wavelengths.

The **Doppler Principle**, discovered by Austrian physicist Christian Doppler in 1842, applies to any type of wave whenever there is relative motion between the source and an observer. This relative motion changes the frequency or wavelength of the observed waves by an amount dependent on the relative line-of-sight velocity. We notice the effect mostly with sound:

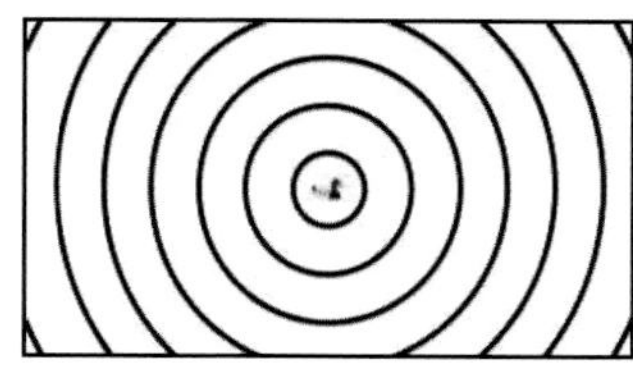

The Doppler Principle is perhaps better understood with moving images and real sounds, so we suggest that you try this YouTube clip out for size:

https://www.youtube.com/watch?v=h4OnBYrbCjY

When light (and radio waves) is received from astronomical sources that are moving away from us, the observed wavelength is longer than it ought to be; when the source is moving towards us, the observed wavelength is shorter.

Thus, the small Doppler shifts in the received wavelengths - these ought to be exactly 21 cm, but are not quite - tell astronomers about the relative velocities of different parts of the Milky Way and hence how it is rotating.

Astronomers use the terms **redshift** and **blueshift** to describe the Doppler shifts in wavelength: redshift applies to receding sources of waves, and blueshift refers to sources that are approaching us.

Which of the following is ***not*** an example of the Doppler Principle?

The decrease in pitch of the sound of a motorcycle as it passes by;

The observed increase in wavelength of a line in the spectrum of a star that is moving away from us;

The decrease in brightness of an Earth-orbiting satellite as it passes into the Earth's shadow;

The observed decrease in wavelength of spectral lines in some galaxies (such as the Andromeda Galaxy) in our Local Group.

Answer after Index

15.2 Groupings of galaxies

In a similar way that stars are found in large collections, galaxies themselves are grouped together on a variety of scales.

On the smallest scale, our Galaxy is a member of **The Local Group**, containing about 50 galaxies that are held together by mutual gravitation; the Group is about 3 megaparsecs (Mpc) across. Other members include:

- the Andromeda Galaxy (M31);
- the Small and Large Magellanic Clouds (SMC and LMC), two small irregular satellite galaxies of the Milky Way;
- the Triangulum Galaxy (M33);
- several small satellite and dwarf galaxies such as Phoenix Dwarf and Aquarius Dwarf.

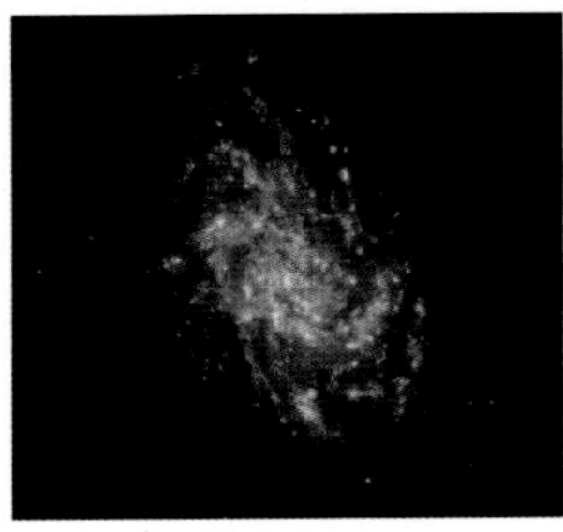

Left and centre: The Triangulum Galaxy (M33) and the Phoenix Dwarf Galaxy: both members of our Local Group. *Image credits: NASA/JPL-Caltech and NASA*

Right: The rich Coma Cluster, containing over 1000 individual galaxies, dominated by two giant ellipticals: the distance to the cluster is ~100 Mpc. *Image credit: NASA/JPL*

There are 5 further groups of galaxies within a distance of 10 Mpc from ours.

On a larger scale, galaxies are found in gravitational agglomerations called rich **clusters** that often contain a giant elliptical galaxy at their centre; they are named after the constellation in which they lie, such as the Virgo, Fornax and Coma clusters. On an even larger scale clusters may compact together under their mutual gravitational attraction to form **superclusters**: our Local Group and the clusters named above are all members of the Virgo Supercluster.

15.3 Classification of galaxies

In the previous section we referred to elliptical, irregular and spiral galaxies. We can now explore these further and introduce the most widespread scheme for classifying galaxies based on their apparent shape: the **Hubble classification system**.

Galaxies are classified as spiral (including barred spiral), elliptical and irregular.

Image credits: NASA

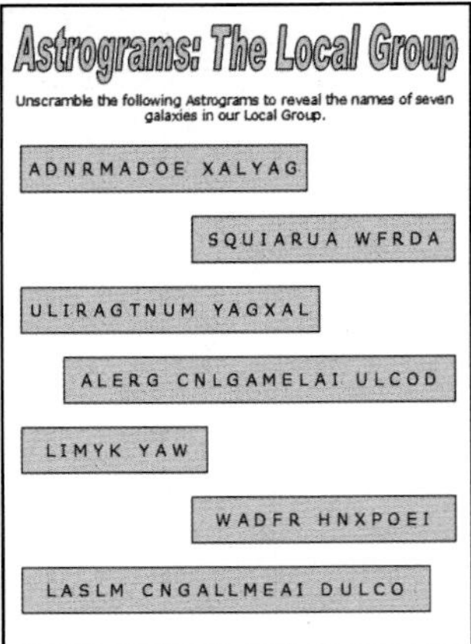

This Astrogram on galaxies in the Local Group is one of an abundance of lesson starters and plenaries contained in our *New Teacher Toolbox for GCSE (9-1) Astronomy* CD-ROM with unlimited site licence.

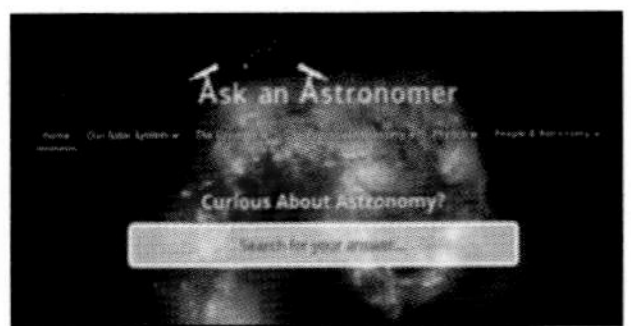

We found a very informative and easy-to-read summary of galaxies and their groupings on a range of scales at the *Ask an Astronomer* website.

There's much more information and answers to lots of questions of the website, but the specific page was:

http://curious.astro.cornell.edu/about-us/100-the-universe/galaxies/groups-and-clusters/545-what-are-collections-of-galaxies-called-intermediate

Galaxy Zoo is part of the larger Zooniverse Project. It invites members of the public (including GCSE Astronomy students and their teachers) to classify galaxies and add them to the databases used by astronomers in puzzling out how galaxies were formed.

www.galaxyzoo.org

Edwin Hubble was an American astronomer who was particularly interested in galaxies. In 1936, Hubble published his book *The Realm of the Nebulae* in which he presented his so-called **Tuning Form Diagram** because of its clear resemblance to a tuning fork. In addition to the basic shapes, the diagram shows sub-divisions within each class; irregular galaxies are not included.

'Equipped with his five senses, man [woman] *explores the Universe around him* [her] *and calls the adventure Science.'*

Edwin Hubble

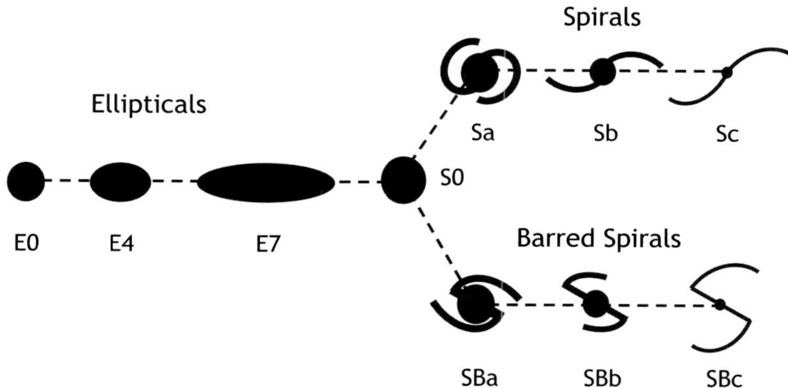

Hubble distinguished between different spiral galaxies by adding letters a, b and c, according to the size of the nucleus and the 'openness' of the spiral arms. He added a number to the elliptical class according to a galaxy's shape. Later versions of the diagram show lenticular galaxies (S0) as an intermediate class between ellipticals and spirals.

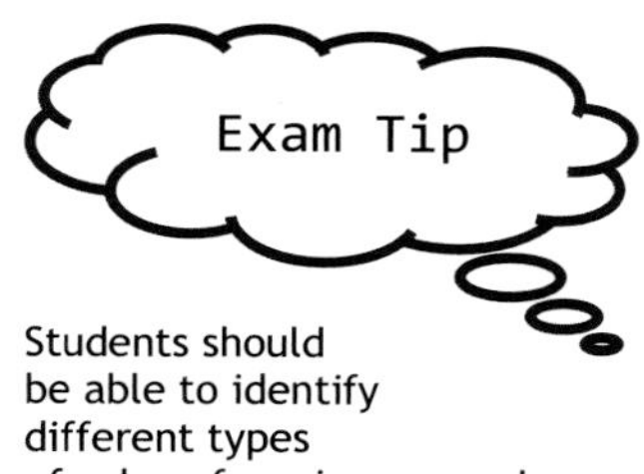

Students should be able to identify different types of galaxy from images and classify them according to Hubble's scheme.

Observational evidence suggests that the first galaxies began to take shape ~13 billion years ago. There are two main theories of galaxy formation:

- Vast clouds of gas and dust collapsed gravitationally, allowing stars to form;
- Large 'lumps' of matter were present in the young Universe. These clumped together under their mutual gravitational attraction to form galaxies. The earliest galaxies were probably spirals that merged to form ellipticals.

15.4 Active galaxies

In addition to 'shining' in the visible part of the spectrum, many galaxies emit huge amounts of radiation in wavebands such as the radio and X-ray regions.

These so-called **active galaxies** have an **Active Galactic Nucleus (AGN)** powered by a central supermassive black hole; the estimated mass is between ~10^6 - 10^9 times greater than a stellar black hole formed during a supernova. The AGN has a huge gravitational influence on nearby stars: it forms an accretion disc in which stellar matter accelerates onto the central black hole and **galactic jets** of electrons and positrons that are emitted in two narrow beams at speeds close to speed of light.

An artist's impression of an AGN: the accretion disc and one of the galactic jets are clearly visible.

Image credit: NASA/Goddard Space Flight Centre Conceptual Image Lab

Historically, astronomers have identified different types of active galaxy, but recent studies suggest that one model can explain their slight differences:

- Seyfert galaxies: these were discovered by astronomer Carl Seyfert in 1943; they have bright nuclei and emit strongly in the IR, UV and X-ray regions;
- Quasars: discovered by Allan Sandage in 1964, these also emit strongly in the UV and X-ray regions, and some are strong emitters of radio waves; quasars appear star-like on images and have large redshifts;
- BL Lacerta Objects - blazars - are compact quasars in which the galactic jets are pointing towards us.

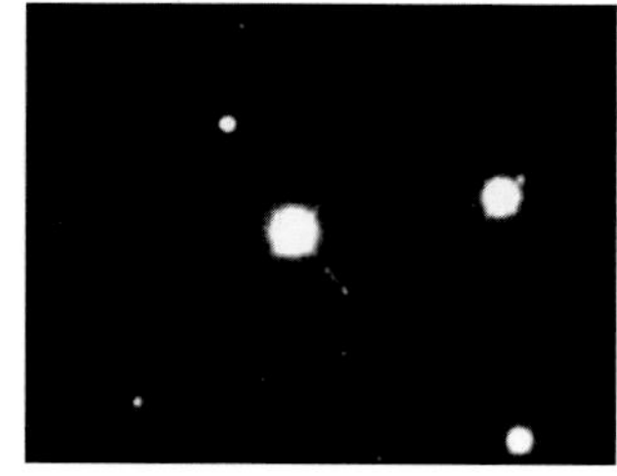

An optical image of star-like 3C 273: this quasar is also a strong emitter of radio waves and X-radiation; one of the bright galactic jets is also (just) visible.

Image credit: NOAO/AURA/NSF

16 Cosmology

16.1 Redshift

16.2 Hubble's law

16.3 The Big Bang

16.1 Redshift

In the 1920s, Edwin Hubble and his assistant Milton Humason used the 100-inch Hooker Telescope at the Mt. Wilson Observatory in California to obtain the spectra of over 50 distant galaxies. They discovered that the wavelengths of the spectral lines were longer than the corresponding wavelengths when measured in the laboratory on Earth.

Part of the Mt. Wilson Observatory near Los Angeles in California. It was using the observatory's 100-inch telescope that Hubble obtained the first redshifted spectra of galaxies.

Image credit: Mt Wilson Observatory

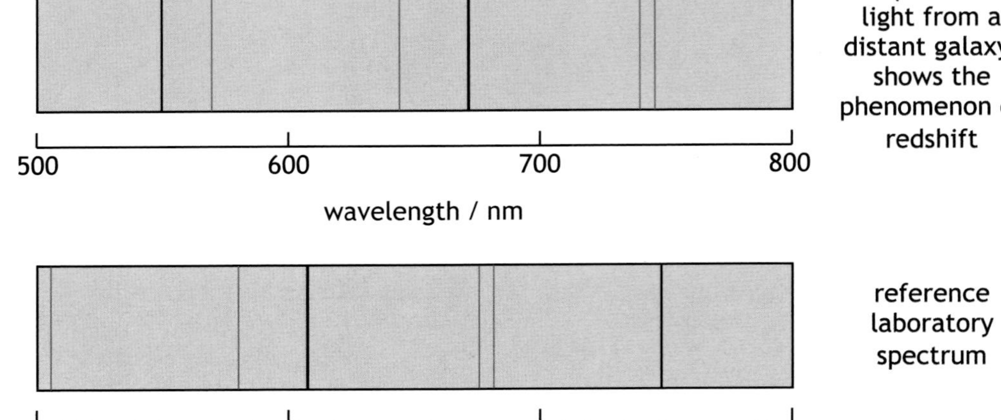

This phenomenon is known as **redshift** (remember that red is the longest wavelength of visible light) and is a further example of the Doppler Principle. It implies that distant galaxies are all moving away from us and not towards us.

The change in wavelength is related to the radial (line-of-sight) velocity (***v***) at which the galaxy is receding by the formula:

$$\frac{\lambda - \lambda_0}{\lambda_0} = \frac{v}{c}$$

Students should be able to use this formula to calculate any of the quantities.

It is important that students are consistent with units: if ***c*** is given in km/s, then ***v*** will also be in km/s; if ***c*** is given in m/s, then ***v*** will also be in m/s.

The *Essential Maths Skills for GCSE (9-1) Astronomy* CD-ROM has plenty of worked examples and practice questions on using this formula.

where λ is the wavelength measured in the spectrum of the galaxy, λ_0 is the true wavelength measured in the laboratory and ***c*** is the speed of light (300 000 km/s or 3.0×10^5 km/s).

It is clear that the larger the redshift, the faster the galaxy is receding.

When the spectrum of quasar 3C 273 (page 65) was obtained in 1965, it showed a redshift of 16%, i.e. the spectral lines were 16% longer than expected. Astronomers deduced that 3C 273 was receding at 16% of the speed of light.

(It is interesting to note that the spectra of some galaxies in our Local Group, including the Andromeda Galaxy, show very slight ***decreases*** in wavelengths due to localised motion ***towards*** us: Andromeda will 'collide' with us one day!)

As the Universe expands, the galaxies (here represented by ladybirds) move further away from each other.

Using increasingly larger telescopes, astronomers have confirmed that all the distant galaxies in the Universe are moving away from us. This indicates that the Universe is expanding and 'dragging' the galaxies with it as it expands.

16.2 Hubble's law

Although determining accurate distances to galaxies was, and still is, very difficult to achieve, Hubble found a linear relationship between the recession velocity (***v***) and distance (***d***).

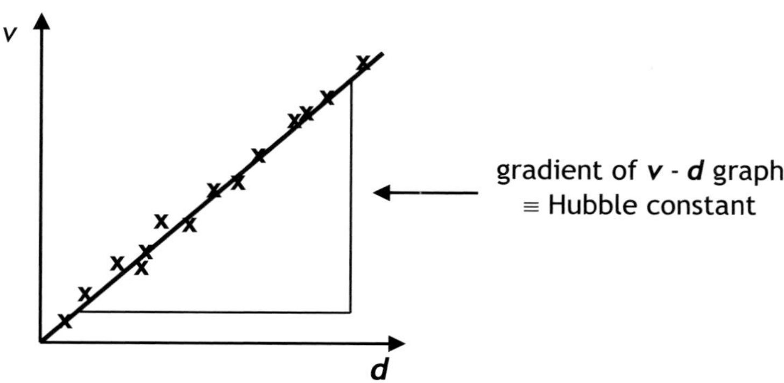

Hubble published this relationship in 1929, and it is now known as **Hubble's law**. In terms of an equation:

$$v = H_0 d$$

where H_0 is the Hubble constant. The value of H_0 can be determined by calculating the gradient of a ***v*** - ***d*** graph; its currently-accepted value is 68 km/s/Mpc (that's 'kilometre per second per megaparsec').

Looking carefully at the unit of H_0, we notice that it contains ***two*** units of length: kilometre and megaparsec. If we convert km into Mpc, we arrive at a very small number with the unit 'per second'.

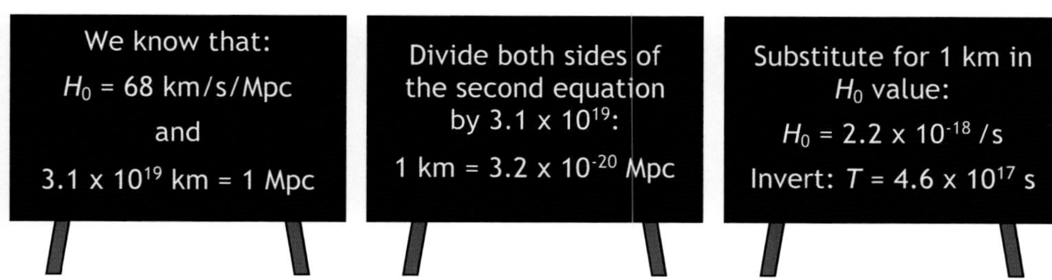

Inverting both the number and unit gives us a very large number in seconds that astronomers call the **Hubble Time (*T*)**; they interpret this as the length of time for which the Universe has been expanding, i.e. the age of the Universe.

A Hubble Time of 4.6 x 10^{17} s corresponds to 14 billion years.

The Hubble constant can also be used to calculate the **Hubble Length**. This can be interpreted as the distance that light has travelled in the Hubble Time, i.e. the size of the Universe.

We know that: distance = (mean or constant) speed x time

We can apply this to cosmology:

Hubble Length = speed of light x Hubble Time

We should point out here that GCSE (9-1) Astronomy students should only understand the methods by which the age and size of the Universe can be estimated; they will not be expected to perform such calculations.

Students may be asked to plot a ***v*** - ***d*** graph given data, and/or to calculate the value of the Hubble constant from such a graph.

When determining the gradient, it is important to draw a ***large*** right-angled triangle.

We found a nice YouTube clip that summarises Hubble's law in 2 minutes, comparing the expansion of the Universe with a giant cookie:

https://www.youtube.com/watch?v=rE0ntbwtFOQ

68 km/s/Mpc

The value of the Hubble constant has a rather odd unit: the kilometre per second per megaparsec.

To understand its meaning a little better, we can break it down into:

kilometre per second

and

per megaparsec.

In other words, for every megaparsec that a galaxy is away from us, it is receding at 68 km/s.

So if a galaxy is 50 Mpc away, it is receding at 50 x 68 km/s.

Now you try one...

A distant galaxy is 800 Mpc away from Earth. Calculate the recession velocity of the galaxy.

Take H_0 as 68 km/s/Mpc

Astronomer, mathematician and Science Fiction writer Fred Hoyle, who coined the term 'Big Bang'.

The internet is full of different 'personal' views about the Big Bang and Steady State models of the Universe, some of which are more convincing than others.

A more 'factual' view can be found at:

http://ester-lisnati.blogspot.co.uk/2011/09/diffrent-between-big-bang-theory-and.html

Arno Penzias and Robert Wilson pose in front of their microwave antenna at the Bell Telephone Laboratories in New Jersey.

Penzias and Wilson accidentally discovered the CMB in 1965 as a uniform 'hiss'; from all parts of the sky at all times of the day. Their discovery gave much support to the Big Bang origin of the Universe.

Image credit: AIP Emilio Segre Visual Archives, Physics Today

The first Hubble Deep Field image

Image credit: NASA

16.3 The Big Bang

Most, but by no means all, astronomers agree that the Universe began as an extremely small, hot, dense event (an 'expansion' rather than an 'explosion') called the **Big Bang** in which space and time came into existence.

It was one of its main opponents, British astronomer Fred Hoyle, who coined the name, allegedly as a derogatory term. Hoyle accepted that the Universe was expanding - there was irrefutable evidence to support this - but he rejected the idea that the Universe had a 'beginning' on philosophical grounds.

Hoyle and his colleagues preferred a 'Steady State' model in which the Universe is and has always been expanding, but with new matter continuously being created so that the overall density of the Universe remains constant.

A third model is that of a 'Cyclic Universe' in which there have been a series of 'Big Bang'/'Big Crunch' scenarios and that these will continue into the future.

The observed expansion of the Universe supports all three models!

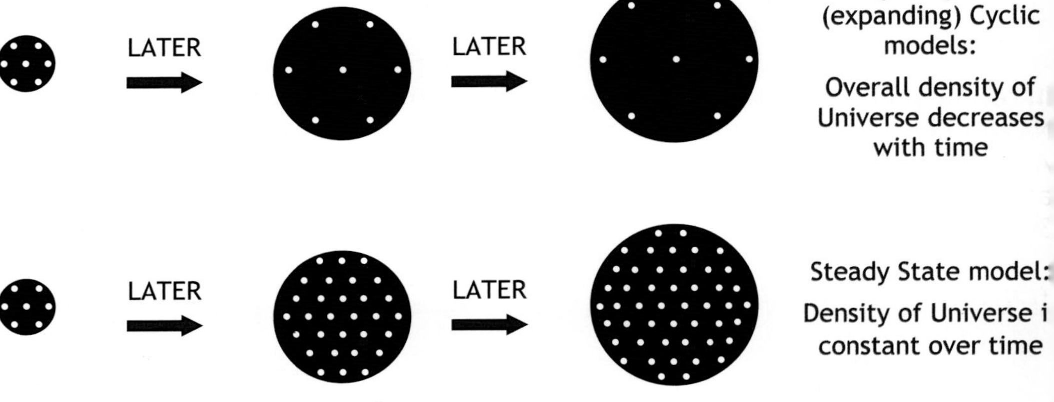

There is, however, a good deal of evidence to support the Big Bang model:

- The existence of **quasars**: these are only found with high redshifts, which implies that they lie great distances from us and were created when the Universe was very young; the fact that quasars were more common in the early Universe compared with today supports the evolutionary nature of the Big Bang model;
- The **cosmic microwave background** (**CMB**) radiation: In 1948, Russian cosmologist George Gamow published a prediction that if the early Universe was hot and dense, it would have cooled as it expanded to a temperature of just a few degrees above absolute zero; in 1965, Arno Penzias and Robert Wilson accidentally discovered the CMB radiation from all parts of the sky that corresponded to a temperature of 2.7 K; this was assigned to be the thermal 'relic' of the Big Bang;
- The **Hubble Deep Field** (**HDF**) **image**: this was the first of a series of long-exposure images of 'empty space' using the Hubble Space Telescope; the field-of-view was only 2.6 arcmin - this was equivalent to the area of a tennis ball 100 m away - but the image revealed many thousands of very distant (and therefore old) galaxies, again implying that the early Universe was very different from how it appears today.

Astronomers are unable to agree on the future evolutionary path of the Universe; the graphic shows four different models.

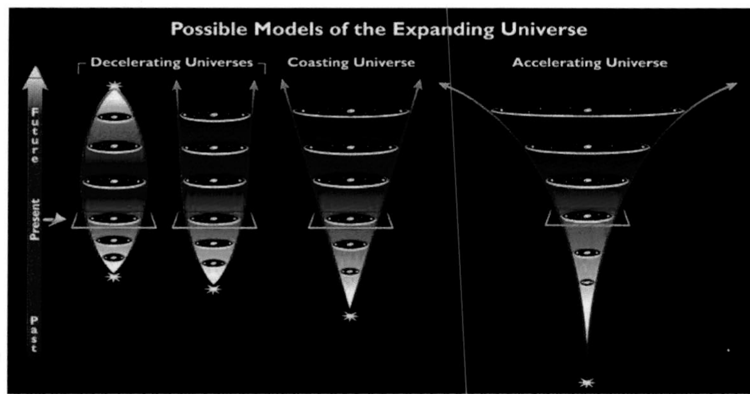

If the expansion of the Universe is decelerating, it will either expand indefinitely or collapse in a 'Big Crunch'.

A so-called 'coasting' Universe will continue to expand at a constant rate.

If the expansion of the Universe is accelerating due to some mysterious repulsive force (so-called **dark energy**), the rate of expansion will increase.

Graphic credit: NASA/ESA

From 2001 until 2010, NASA's *Wilkinson Microwave Anisotropy Probe* studied minute fluctuations in the CMB radiation.

Image credit: NASA

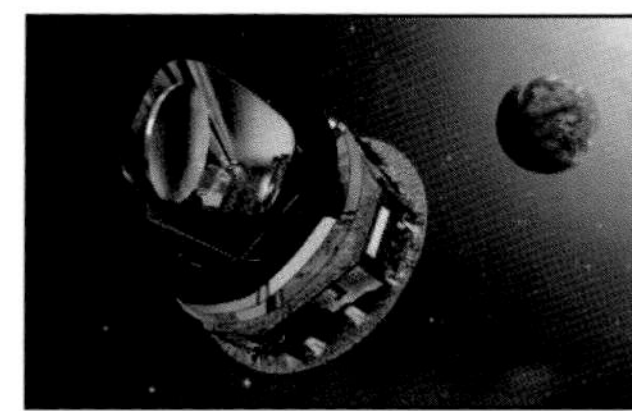

An artist's impression of ESA's *Planck* observatory, shielded from the Sun at the Earth's L2 Lagrangian Point.

Between 2009 and 2015, Planck's instruments studied anisotropies in the CMB.

Image credit: ESA

In recent years, observations of tiny fluctuations in the CMB made by the NASA's *Cosmic Background Explorer* (COBE) satellite, its *Wilkinson Microwave Anisotropy Probe* (WMAP) and ESA's *Planck* observatory have allowed astronomers to study the edge of the visible Universe at a time when it was just 380 000 years old.

'Planck is like the Ferrari of CMB missions.'

Krzysztof Gorski, Planck scientist

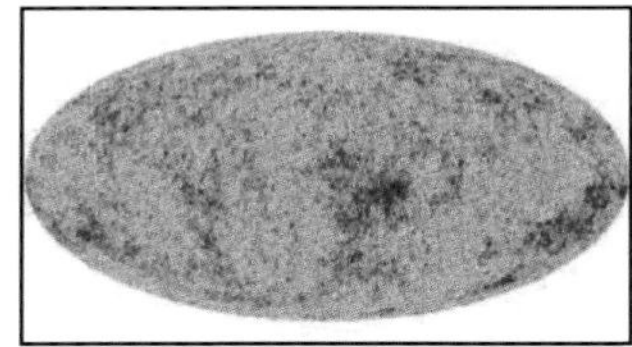

An all-sky map of the CMB imaged by the *Planck* observatory.

The exaggerated differences in colour show tiny temperature fluctuations that correspond to regions of different densities in the early Universe; the slightly denser regions are thought to have been the foundations for the creation of stars and galaxies.

Image credit: ESA/Planck

Major results from these space missions have revealed that:

- the Universe is slightly older than was previously thought;
- approximately 25% of the Universe is composed of invisible **dark matter**;
- there is no evidence to invalidate the theory of **cosmic inflation** (the very rapid, uniform expansion of the Universe shortly after the Big Bang).

Our understanding of the structure and evolution of the Universe has been greatly enhanced by results from recent space missions, but there are still many unresolved issues, particularly the existence and likely nature of the aforementioned **dark matter** and **dark energy**.

These make up approximately 95% of the known Universe, but at the present time, astronomers are unable to see, detect or even comprehend them.

Astronomers use the likely existence of dark matter to explain **gravitational lensing** - the apparent 'bending' of light from galaxies to form multiple images of the same galaxy - and many agree that it may exist in the form of exotic particles called WIMPs (Weakly Interacting Massive Particles).

However, astronomers are less certain about the nature dark energy. Perhaps it will be during the lifetime of the current GCSE Astronomy specification that our understanding of this mysterious force that appears to be accelerating the Universe's expansion will be better understood.

Index

Answers to  Questions

Page 5: (a) Bandung, Indonesia: 107° E, 7° S; (b) Quingdao, China: 120° E, 36° N; (c) Minsk, Belarus: 28° E, 54° N; (d) Lima, Peru: 74° W, 12° S. **Page 6**: The Merry-go-round at the End of the Pier.

Page 9: (1) Polaris; (2a) 6 h 45 min, -17°; (b) 5 h 55 min, +7°; (c) 22 h 58 min, -30°; (d) 20 h 41 min, +45°

Page 10: (1) 05:35; (2) 45 min; (3) 30 min. **Page 11**: (1a) 44°; (b) 28°; (c) 51°; (d) 27°; (2a) True; (b) True.

Page 13: (a) True; (b) False; (c) False; (d) True. **Page 14**: (1) 9.1 days; (2) 12 astronauts.

Page 18: (1) Saturn; (2) Mars; (3) Venus. **Page 23**: 6.25 **Page 25**: (a) False; (b) True; (c) False.

Page 26: (1) 6.2 AU; (2) 1.72 AU. **Page 28**: Mercury, Venus, Mars, Jupiter & Saturn. **Page 32**: 64

Page 34: (1) 10 days; (2) 33 days. **Page 37**: 71 years.

Page 40: 3 (to the nearest whole number); Moon passes through the centre of Earth's umbra.

Page 41: 47° is ***twice*** 23.5° (the latitudes of the Tropics). **Page 42**: February **Page 43**: (a) True; (b) False; (c) False; (d) True. **Page 45**: Joe is further west, by 25° of longitude.

Page 50: 30 000 km **Page 54**: (a) γ Cas; (b) β Cyg; (c) α Psc; (d) δ Her.

Page 54: B1, A6, F1, G0, G2, K4, K7. **Page 58**: The **largest distance** between any two radio telescopes in an array.

Page 63: The drop in brightness of an Earth-orbiting satellite. **Page 67**: 54 400 km/s